New Snapshot Pre-Intermediate
Language Booster

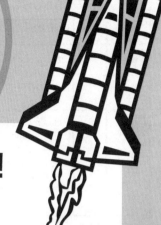

Welcome to the Language Booster!

This book will give you lots of extra practice, not just in grammar, but also in vocabulary and communication skills.

The Workbook

The Language Booster starts off with a **Workbook** section (pages 4 to 83). It's a workbook with a difference – the exercises are separated into three levels: *Stay cool* (easy exercises), *Move on* (harder exercises) and *Go for it* (challenging exercises). You and your teacher can choose the level that suits you best, or you can work through all the exercises if you like! When you feel confident with one level, you can move on to the next level.

After every two units, you will find a page designed to help you develop and improve your writing skills. It's called *Boost your Writing*.

The Grammar Builder

Do you still need more grammar practice? The second part of the Language Booster (pages 84 to 144) is called the **Grammar Builder** and contains an extra bank of grammar practice exercises and includes grammar reference sections called *Grammar highlights*, so that you can check on grammar rules when you are doing the exercises. You can work through the units in the Grammar Builder alongside the units in the Workbook section, or you can do them at a later stage for revision.

We hope that this Language Booster, with its special features, will give you all the help you need to learn English successfully – and enjoyably!

Workbook: Chris Barker, Brian Abbs, Ingrid Freebairn
Grammar Builder: Olivia Johnston

Contents

1 Do you live here?

Vocabulary

Stay cool

1 What do you call the people who do these things? Change the verbs into nouns.

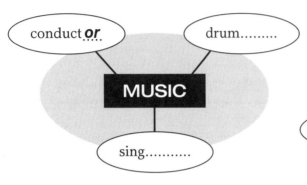

conduct **or** ..... / drum......... → MUSIC → sing...........

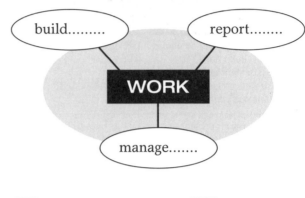

build......... / report........ → WORK → manage.......

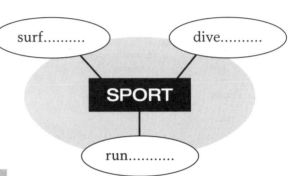

surf......... / dive.......... → SPORT → run...........

Move on / Go for it

2 Complete the crossword.

¹S	U	²R	F	E	³R		⁴ ⁵ ⁶

(crossword grid)

Across

1 I'm a professional ... , so I travel everywhere with my surfboard. (6)
4 'How ... are you?' 'I'm about 1.8 metres.' (4)
7 She can drive, but she hasn't got a ... . (3)
8 Can I borrow your mobile ... , please? (5)
9 How ... are you in London for? (4)
11 'How often do the buses come?' 'There's ... every hour.' (3)
12 'Can he ... a horse?' 'Yes, he's a good rider.' (4)
14 There are six English ... at our school, and two of them also teach German. (8)
17 I'm studying at drama school because I want to be an ... . (5)
18 Does this bus ... to the beach? (2)
19 I was so late, I ... all the way to school! (3)
20 I build houses. I'm a ... . (7)
22 I usually come here with ... parents. (2)
23 He likes St Ives because he likes being near the ... . (3)

Down

1 I haven't got a boat, but I'm a good ... . (6)
2 I do the London Marathon every year, but I'm not a professional ... . (6)
3 I work for a newspaper as a ... . (8)
4 When you sit in the sun you get a ... . (3)
5 'I'm a surfer.' '... you?' (3)
6 Hard ... ! (4)
7 He's the ... of a famous orchestra. (9)
10 Are you here ... holiday? (2)
13 We're here with ... parents. (3)
14 I'm here ... work. (2)
15 Tania ... about 25 dollars a day. (5)
16 The weather's great. The ... shines every day. (3)
18 'Let's walk.' 'No, I'm tired. Let's ... the bus.' (3)
20 My name's Matt, ... the way. (2)
21 Sydney is ... Australia. (2)

Stay cool

Present simple and continuous

3 Use the pictures to write the questions or the answers using the verbs in the box.

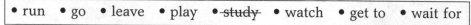

• run • go • leave • play • ~~study~~ • watch • get to • wait for

A: *What's she studying?*

B: Italian.

1 **A:** What are they doing?

   B: .... bus.

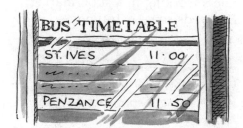

2 **A:** .... St Ives?

   B: It leaves at eleven o'clock.

   A: And .... Penzance?

   B: At 11.50.

3 **A:** Is he going to the beach?

   B: .... He ....

4 **A:** What are you two doing?

   B and C: .... a film.

5 **A:** What do you do in your free time?

   B: .... and ....

Infinitive of purpose

4 Match the sentence halves.

1 They go to the USA every year

2 He's saving money

3 I'm going to the bank

4 She does yoga

5 I'm writing to the hotel manager

6 We're going into town

7 I'm phoning Mum

8 I walk to school

a) to ask her to record *Top of the Pops* for me.

b) to change some money.

c) to go to Australia next year.

d) to help her relax.

e) to meet our friends.

f) to save money.

g) to ask for a part-time job.

h) to see their American cousins.

1 *h*   2 ......   3 ......   4 ......   5 ......   6 ......   7 ......   8 ......

Move on

Present simple and continuous

5 Complete the e-mails using the verbs in the present simple or continuous.

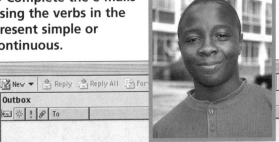

Hi, Kirsty

What (you / do) *are you doing?* (I / not do) ¹........................ anything at the moment. In fact, (I / go) ²........................ crazy because I'm really bored. That's why (I / write) ³........................ to you. Mum and Dad (do / the shopping) ⁴........................ .... (I / hate) ⁵........................ shopping, so I'm here alone. (you / want) ⁶........................ to go out this afternoon?

Laurie

Hi, Laurie

Thanks for the e-mail. So when you're bored (you / write) ⁷........................ to me. That's nice. Actually, I can't go out this afternoon. I've got a Saturday job at the hairdresser's in Long Lane. It's great! (I / not start) ⁸........................ until two and (I / work) ⁹........................ until eight, but that's OK. The manager there is really nice to the Saturday people. (We / get) ¹⁰........................ a share of the tips!

Why (you / sit) ¹¹........................ at home today? (Lots of teenagers / have) ¹²........................ part-time jobs. Go out and get one!

Kirsty

Infinitive of purpose

6 Join the sentences using the infinitive of the verbs in the box to describe these people's plans.

• study • visit • ~~learn~~ • earn • raise

Carol wants to speak Spanish. She's going to Madrid for three months.

Carol's going to Madrid for three months *to learn Spanish.*

1 Bob's working in a supermarket. He needs some extra money.

....

....

2 We need money for our school. We're doing a sponsored swim.

....

....

3 Shari's going to college. She's got a place on the Law course.

....

....

4 My grandmother's ill. I'm going to the hospital.

....

....

Go for it

7 In your notebook, write an e-mail to a friend.
- Say why you're writing.
- Say what you want to do.
- Ask if your friend wants to join you.

Communication

Stay cool

8 Write the correct echo questions.

> • Are you? • Is he? • Is she? • Do you?
> • Have they?

> **A:** Anna's going out with Oliver.
>
> **B:** *Is she?* ....

1 **A:** My brother's in a rock band.

  B: .... ?

2 **A:** We're learning the guitar.

  B: .... ?

3 **A:** I still like the Backstreet Boys.

  B: .... ?

4 **A:** Our friends have got a house near the beach.

  B: .... ?

Move on

9 Complete the conversations.

> **A:** Are you a student?
>
> **B:** Yes, *I am* .... I'm doing a Business Studies course.
>
> **A:** *Are you?* .... My sister's on a Business Studies course, too.

1 **A:** My parents are renting out a room in our house.

  B: .... ? Who are they renting it to?

  A: A drummer in a rock band.

  B: .... a lot of noise?

  A: No, you never .... him.

2 **A:** I've got a book about painters in St Ives.

  B: .... ? That's interesting.

  .... a look at it?

  A: Sure.

3 **A:** My cousins usually spend the summer with us.

  B: .... ? How many cousins

  .... ?

  A: Ten.

  B: .... ? That's a lot!

Go for it

10 In your notebook, continue the conversation between Natalie and Jack. Natalie works as a pool attendant at the Solara Leisure Centre.

Jack asks Natalie:
* where the leisure centre is;
* about her job;
* about the opening hours;
* about what there is at the centre;
* how much it costs to join the gym.

Jack: *Excuse me, is the leisure centre near here?*

Natalie: *Yes, it is. It's on Thorpe Road. I'm going there now.*

Jack: *Are you?* ...

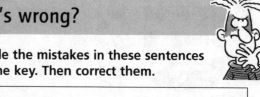

Open 7 a.m. to 10 p.m.

Gym, swimming pool, badminton and squash courts

Membership fees
£350 per year

Solara Leisure Centre
Thorpe Road

What's wrong?

11 Circle the mistakes in these sentences using the key. Then correct them.

> **Key**
> p = punctuation   w.o. = word order
> gr = grammar   sp = spelling
> ^ = there is a word missing v = vocabulary

sp That's (briliant!)
That's brilliant!
....

1 ...... Where does he comes from?

....

2 ...... My father is doctor.

....

3 ...... We come here usually in the summer.

....
....

4 ...... I'm looking for a part-time work.

....
....

5 .... Are you australian?

....

2 Over three hours late.

Vocabulary

Stay cool / Move on

1 Write the names of the means of transport (1–9) to find the missing word (10).

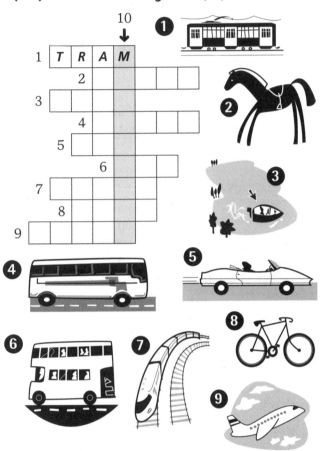

10 ↓

1	T	R	A	M
	2			
3				
	4			
5				
	6			
7				
8				
9				

2 Write in the missing words. Then number the phrases in sequence from distant past to recent past.

• last • yesterday • ago

a) five minutes .... ☐

b) .... month ☐

c) this afternoon ☐

d) this morning ☐

e) three months .... ☐

f) two days .... ☐

g) .... afternoon ☐

h) .... week ☐

i) *last* .... year ☐ **1**

j) .... night ☐

k) .... morning ☐

Go for it

3 Complete the dialogue.

Teacher: George, you were late _yesterday_ morning and you're late again ¹...................... morning. Why?

George: Well, ²...................... weekend I played in a football match. I tripped and hurt my leg, so I couldn't cycle to school ³............... Monday. I left home ⁴.................. eight o'clock, but the walk to school took ages.

Teacher: You seemed fine ⁵........................ lunchtime yesterday. You were playing football in the playground.

George: Oh, yes, I felt much better then.

Teacher: And what about ⁶........... morning?

George: Well, my dog escaped ⁷................. night. It took me hours to find it. I finally got to bed ⁸............... two o'clock, so I was quite tired.

Teacher: Really? I thought your dog died three months ⁹...................... .

George: Oh, er, yes, that one did. This is another one.

Teacher: George.

George: Yes, Miss Perkins.

Teacher: Stay behind after school and write 200 words on 'Excuses for being late'.

George: Yes, Miss Perkins.

Grammar

Stay cool

Past simple
Linkers

4 Describe Leo's day at the beach with his friends. Look at the pictures and use these phrases.

• And then	• go for a bike ride
• After that	• go swimming
• ~~First of all~~	• have a barbecue
• After lunch	• have lunch
• Then	• ~~play volleyball~~
• In the evening	• relax

First of all, we played volleyball. ....

....

....

....

....

....

Conjunctions *so* and *because*

5 Match the two halves of the sentences, and link them with *so* or *because*.

1 Matt didn't know which bus to take

2 Nicola's train was late

3 Matt's in Cornwall

4 Nicola tripped over her shoes

5 Matt and Nicola both wanted the 53 bus

6 Nicola's going to relax

so

because

a) she's clumsy.

b) she's tired.

c) he asked Nicola.

d) she phoned her aunt.

e) there's a surfing competition there.

f) they travelled together.

Move on

Past simple

6 Complete the text by putting the verbs in brackets in the correct past tense form.

1500 Leonardo da Vinci (design) *designed* a helicopter.

1620 Cornelius van Drebbel (build) [1]....................... a submarine.

1783 Pilâtre de Rozier and the Marquis d'Arlandes (make) [2]....................... the first flight in a hot-air balloon.

1791 Comte Mede de Sivrac (design) [3]........................... a bicycle without pedals.

1829 George Stephenson's locomotive *The Rocket* (win) [4].............. a competition.

1837 Steam trams (begin) [5]....................... to operate in New York City.

1843 The *Great Britain* steamship (sail) [6].................... across the Atlantic Ocean.

1863 The first underground railway (open) [7]....................... in London.

1885 Karl Benz and Gottlieb Daimler (invent) [8]....................... the petrol engine.

1909 Louis Blériot (fly) [9]....................... from France to England in a monoplane.

Go for it

Past simple
Conjunctions *so* and *because*

7 Complete the captions using *so* or *because* and the past simple tense.

His team was very pleased *because he scored* two goals.

1 We only had lessons in the mornings .... to the beach every afternoon.

2 He was annoyed with me .... on his toe.

3 They had to walk .... enough money for the bus.

4 The shop assistant was rude to Mrs Stubbs .... to the manager.

5 I needed to earn some money .... as a waitress.

Past simple
Linkers

8 Complete Sophia's account of her school trip using these verbs and linkers.

Verbs

• arrive • buy • feel • travel • get on
• ~~go~~ • have • leave • see • take
• take • think • visit • not have
• not sleep • not want

Linkers

• after breakfast • first of all • ~~last week~~
• in the afternoon • before lunch

School trip to Amsterdam

Last week , 30 students from my school
went on a school trip to The Netherlands.
We ¹......... school at two o'clock on
Thursday afternoon and we ²........... the
boat at about eight o'clock. The crossing
³.................. nine hours. Unfortunately, we
⁴.................. cabins, so we ⁵....................
very well. Anyway, we ⁶...................... in
Rotterdam on Friday morning. We ⁷...........
breakfast and we all ⁸...................... much
better. ⁹... , we
¹⁰........................... by coach to Amsterdam.
In Amsterdam, we did a lot. ¹¹.............. ,
we ¹²...................... the Van Gogh museum.
I ¹³.................. it was really interesting.
¹⁴............................... , I ¹⁵...................
some things from the museum shop. We had
lunch outside.
¹⁶......................... , our teachers ¹⁷............
us on a tram into the old part of the city.
We ¹⁸.................. the canals and the old
buildings. Then we had to get the coach
back to Rotterdam to catch the ferry
home. I ¹⁹............................. to leave!

Communication

Stay cool

9 Complete the dialogue.

A: _Where did you go_ last weekend?

B: I went to York to see a friend at the university.

A: Did you? [1] .... ?

B: By coach.

A: Really? [2] .... ?

B: Four hours.

A: [3] .... ?

B: It wasn't too bad.

A: [4] .... in York?

B: We just walked around during the day and went to the theatre in the evening.

Move on / Go for it

10 In your notebook, write a dialogue between you and a friend from London using the prompts.

You: (where / go?)
Where did you go for your holidays?

Friend: _I went to the Isle of Skye._

Isle of Skye
Scotland

You: (how / travel?)

Friend: ....

You: (how long / take?)

07:00 → 20:00

Friend: ....

You: (what / do there?)

....

Friend:

too cold!

What's wrong?

11 Circle and correct the mistakes.

I came to this school (before three years.)
I came to this school three years ago.

1 I saw her the last week.

....

2 I didn't bought anything.

....

3 I stayed at my friend's house yesterday night.

....

....

4 Where you went last weekend?

....

5 **A:** Was your journey OK?
  B: It could be worse.

....

CULTURE SNAPSHOT

Holidays

The top five tourist destinations in the world are the USA, France, Italy, Spain and the UK. Most visitors to the UK are from the USA and France.

To get from France to England, you can fly, you can go by boat or you can go by train through the Channel Tunnel. There are two types of train through the tunnel: the Shuttle is for cars, motorbikes and coaches; Eurostar is for foot passengers.

ENGLAND
Dover
Folkestone
The English Channel
Calais
FRANCE

Boost your Writing 1

Text: Write a formal letter

1 Read the advertisements for summer jobs and list the jobs.

waiters / waitresses

....

....

....

....

....

Come and work at Blackpool Holiday Park!

Restaurants
We need people to work in our restaurants as waiters and waitresses. Staff serve food and do general cleaning.

Shops
The shops in the park include a supermarket and a children's fun shop. Shop assistants help customers. Cashiers work on the cash desks.

Reception
Receptionists work on the reception desk, answering the phones, making reservations and helping guests.

Leisure
We employ a team of leisure assistants to look after children and to organise games and activities for them.

Accommodation
Our room attendants prepare the rooms for guests, clean the bathrooms and make the beds.

2 Read Karina's letter and match these features to the correct letter (A–F).

- her address [A]
- the title and address of the person she is writing to [ ]
- a phrase to close a formal letter [ ]
- the date [ ]
- her name [ ]
- a phrase to start a formal letter [ ]

3 Read the letter again and match each topic to the correct section (1–6).

Past experience [ ]

Reasons she would be good at the job [ ]

Reason for writing [1]

Referees (people who can support her application) [ ]

Details of her education [ ]

Personal details (age) [ ]

4 In your notebook, write a letter applying for one of the jobs in Exercise 1.

A

12 Bennets Road
Cheltenham
Gloucestershire
GL49 5YG
3rd March

B

The Manager
Blackpool Holiday Park
PO Box 67 **C**
Blackpool
FY3 4TU **D**

Dear Sir/Madam, **1**

I am writing to apply for a job as a waitress at the Holiday Park this summer.

I am seventeen years old, but I will be eighteen in April. **2**

I go to Highgrove School in Cheltenham, where I am studying for my **3** A Levels in English, French and German.

Last summer, I worked on a farm in Somerset. I liked the job, **4** and I got on well with the other people there.

I enjoy working with people of all ages. I speak French and German, so I could talk to guests who speak those languages. **5**

My referees are Mrs Sian Thomas, Highgrove School, Cheltenham, Gloucestershire, GL37 6EU and Mr Jack Higgins, 12 Linden Avenue, Stroud, Gloucestershire, GL15 9JB. **6**

Mrs Thomas is my French teacher and Mr Higgins is a family friend.

I look forward to hearing from you.

Yours faithfully, **E**

Karina Watkins

(Ms KARINA WATKINS) **F**

3 A view which excites me.

Vocabulary

Stay cool

1 Use the words in the box to label the pictures.

> • a bay • a̶ ̶b̶e̶a̶c̶h̶ • a field • a forest
> • a hill • a lake • a mountain • a river
> • a tree • a valley • an island • cliffs
> • rocks • the sea

1 ....

2 ....

3 ....

4 ....

5 ....

a beach

6 ....

12 ....

11 ....

7 ....

13 ....

8 ....

10 ....

9 ....

Move on

2 Answer the questions.

How good is your geography?

> Try this quiz. Use the extra clues if you need to.

The Black *Forest* is a famous area in SW Germany.

1 New Zealand consists of two .... , North and South.

2 Mount Everest, Ben Nevis and K2 are ....

3 The Nile, the Danube and the Ganges are ....

4 The USA is between the Atlantic and the Pacific ....

5 Michigan, Superior, Huron, Ontario and Erie are sometimes called the Great ....

6 The .... of the Kings is in Egypt, near the River Nile.

Extra clues:	A lot of trees together	**1** Land surrounded by water	**2** Bigger than hills
	3 They run, but they can't walk!	**4** Bigger than seas	**5** Smaller than seas
	6 Land between two lines of hills		

Go for it

3 In your notebook, make up a geography quiz about the natural environment in your country.

Stay cool

Future with *going to*, *will* or present continuous

4 Circle the correct response.

Slow down. What's the rush?

a) We're missing the bus!

b) We'll miss the bus! *(circled)*

1 Have you got any plans for the weekend?

a) Yes, we're going to visit my cousins.

b) Yes, we'll visit my cousins.

2 Don't go near the edge of the cliff!

a) It's OK. I won't fall.

b) It's OK. I'm not falling.

3 Do your exams start soon?

a) Yes, I'm taking Science and Maths next week.

b) Yes, I'll take Science and Maths next week.

4 Do you want to go out this evening?

a) Sorry, we're seeing Alex later.

b) Sorry, we'll see Alex later.

5 We're so late!

a) They'll wait, don't worry.

b) They're going to wait, don't worry.

6 See you at the café later.

a) OK. I'm going to meet there you at seven.

b) OK. I'll meet you there at seven.

Defining and non-defining relative clauses

5 Complete the sentences with *who*, *which* or *where*.

Students Why is homework sometimes a problem?

You've got a little brother *who*'s great, but ¹..................... makes a lot of noise.

Your older sister, ²..................... is at college, needs the computer to do her work.

You've got a room ³..................... is too small.

What's the answer?

The Computer and Homework Club

- Students ⁴..................... have problems doing homework at home can come here and work.
- We have a large room ⁵..................... students can do homework and a computer room with programs ⁶..................... are specifically designed to help with school work.
- We also have some programs ⁷..................... are purely for fun.
- There will always be somebody ⁸..................... will help you.
- The club, ⁹..................... is close to Ladbroke Grove, is open from 3.30 to 6.00 p.m.

Anything else?

- Our computer courses, ¹⁰..................... are free for students under 16, take place on Monday and Wednesday evenings.
- And we have a coffee bar ¹¹..................... you can meet other students.

• Move on

Future with *going to, will* or present continuous
Defining and non-defining relative clauses

6 Use the prompts with *'ll (will), going to* or the present continuous to complete the first part of the conversation.

Simon: Oh, no!

Jack: What's the problem?

Simon: (Kate / come round) *Kate's coming round* in half an hour. I'm making her a surprise cake for her birthday, but (it / not be) [1].................. ready.

Jack: Phone and tell her to come round tomorrow.

Simon: (She / go) [2].......................... to her grandparents' tomorrow.

Jack: Well, go out and buy a cake.

Simon: No, no, (I / not buy) [3]........................ .... one.

Jack: Why don't you take her to the cinema for her birthday instead? (She / like) [4]............................ that.

Simon: That's a good idea. (I / phone) [5]................................. the Trocadero to see what's on.

Jack: OK. What (you / do) [6]........................ .... with the cake mixture?

Simon: I think (I / put) [7]............................... it in the fridge.

Now complete the second part of the conversation with the relative pronouns *who, which* or *where*.

Jack: The Trocadero is the cinema *where* I went with Yvonne on our first date. It's the one [8]....................... has got an enormous screen and fantastic sound.

Simon: Excellent.

Jack: And there's a place next door [9]................. they serve brilliant pizzas.

Simon: Even better.

Jack: And I know someone [10]....................... works there as a waiter. I think you're going to have a great evening!

• Go for it

7 Use the notes to write about Elena's plans. In each sentence include *going to, will* or the present continuous, and a clause beginning *who, which* or *where.*

next week: see the careers advisor (she comes to our school)

Next week, I'm seeing / I'm going to see the careers advisor who comes to our school.

1 next year: spend some time in an English-speaking country (I can get a part-time job)

....
....
....

2 then: probably go to Watford College (it's close to my grandmother's house)

....
....
....

3 do a course in Office Skills (it's useful for secretarial work or business)

....
....
....

4 stay with my grandmother (she lives near Watford)

....
....
....

Now write a sentence in your notebook about your plans for further education / a career.

Stay cool

8 Fill in the missing words. Then rewrite the conversation in the correct order in your notebook.

☐ What are you .... on Saturday evening?

☐ Yes. That .... be great.

☐ Yes, I'm quite busy. I'm .... out on Tuesday and I think I'm .... in a volleyball match on Thursday.

☐ Because I've got two tickets for the concert at the Apollo. Do you .... coming?

1 *Are* you busy next week?

☐ Saturday? I'm not sure. Why?

A: *Are you busy next week?*

Move on

9 Continue this conversation using the prompts.

A: you / do / weekend?
What are you doing at the weekend?

B: help / open-air concert at school / Saturday
1 ....
....

A: free / Sunday?
2 ....
....

B: ✓
3 ....
....

A: fancy / go / bike ride along the river?
4 ....
....

B: ✓
5 ....
....

A: phone / Saturday evening
6 ....
....

Go for it

10 Invite a friend to go on a camping trip. He/She can't go this weekend, but next weekend is possible. Write the conversation in your notebook.

You: *Are you busy this weekend?*

Friend: *Yes, ...*

What's wrong?

11 Circle and correct the mistakes.

We'll meet at eight, if (thats) all right.
We'll meet at eight, if that's all right.

1 Students which are late must report to the office.
....

2 She lives on an iland.
....

3 It's a place where live many artists.
....

4 Do you fancy go out tonight?
....

5 I talk to you later.
....

STUDY CORNER

Noting context

When you learn a new expression, note down the context in which it is used and the translation.

12 In your notebook, write the context and the translation of these expressions, which include *will*.

Expression	Context	Translation
I'll go.	*When the doorbell or the phone rings*	
I'll see you later. I'll have a coffee. I'll do it for you. I'll think about it. I'll take the blue one, please.		

4 How long have you been here?

Vocabulary

Stay cool

1 Complete the captions by using the adjectives in their positive and negative forms.

- formal
- mature
- successful
- ~~pleasant~~
- correct

a) _a pleasant_ smell

b) _an unpleasant_ smell

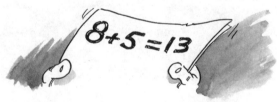

1 a) .... answer

b) .... answer

2 a) 16-year-old

b) 16-year-old

3 a) .... dinner

b) .... dinner

4 a) .... writer

b) .... writer

Move on

2 Complete the adjectives.

I'd really like you to come on Thursday. Would that be po _ssible_ ?

1 Everybody likes him. He's very po.......... .

2 You eat well. That's why you're so he.......... .

3 I couldn't put the book down. It was really in........................... .

4 She buys all the latest clothes. She's very fa........................ .

5 A lot depends on this exam. It's im.......... .

Go for it

3 Write pairs of sentences in your notebook to illustrate the opposite of the adjectives in Exercise 2.

Sorry, I can't come on Thursday. It's impossible.

Stay cool

Present perfect simple with *for* and *since*

4 Write sentences using the present perfect with *for* or *since*.

I / not clean / my room / ages

I haven't cleaned my room for ages.

1 He / work / barman / June

   ....
   ....

2 they / be away / three weeks?

   ....
   ....

3 I / not ride / a horse / I was a child

   ....
   ....

4 You / not write / to Julia / a long time

   ....
   ....

5 We / not have / a curry / we were in London

   ....
   ....

6 you / see / Adam / the party?

   ....
   ....

7 I / not speak / to Harry / months

   ....
   ....

8 She / live / in Paris / a year

   ....
   ....

Comparison of adjectives

5 Use the adjectives to make comparisons.

Travelling by coach isn't *as comfortable as* (comfortable) travelling by train.

Travelling by train is *faster* (fast) than travelling by coach.

Travelling by plane is *the fastest* (fast) of all.

1 He isn't .... (tall) his sister.

2 He's .... (short) than his sister.

3 She's .... (tall) girl in the school.

4 His second album wasn't .... (good) his first album.

5 His third album was .... (bad) than his second album.

6 His most recent album was .... (bad) album he's made.

7 Rollerblading isn't .... (expensive) skiing.

8 Snowboarding is .... (exciting) than rollerblading.

9 Swimming is .... (cheap) sport of all.

In which three sentences can you use *much*?

....

Move on

Present perfect simple with *for* and *since*

6 Rewrite each sentence in two ways, using *for* and *since*.

She last went to the gym on February 1st.
(not do / any exercise)

She hasn't done any exercise since February 1st.
She hasn't done any exercise for three weeks.

1 I last went to the hairdresser's in March.
(not go / the hairdresser's)

....

....

2 We joined the queue at 12.30.
(be / in the queue)

....

....

March 28th

Dear Mrs Rainford
Please note that your car's first service
is now due.

3 My mum bought her car a year ago.
(have / her car)

....

....

4 He got on the bus at 4.30
(be / on the bus)

....

....

7 Make comparisons about these places.
Use *much* where it is appropriate.

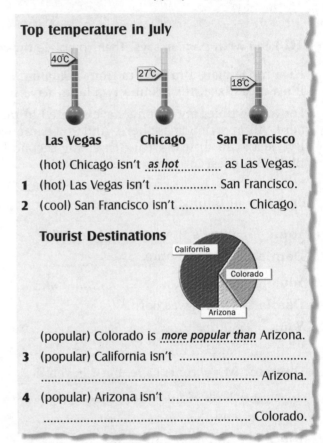

Top temperature in July

Las Vegas 40°C   Chicago 27°C   San Francisco 18°C

(hot) Chicago isn't *as hot* as Las Vegas.

1 (hot) Las Vegas isn't .... San Francisco.

2 (cool) San Francisco isn't .... Chicago.

Tourist Destinations

California   Colorado   Arizona

(popular) Colorado is *more popular than* Arizona.

3 (popular) California isn't ....
.... Arizona.

4 (popular) Arizona isn't ....
.... Colorado.

Go for it

Comparison of adjectivess

8 In your notebook, write about yourself and
your family. Use these words to help you.

- tidy • friendly • confident
- independent • clever • practical
- funny • sporty • mature

I've got a sister and a brother.

I'm not as tidy as ...

Stay cool

9 Complete the questions and the answers. Then match them.

Questions	Answers
1 *Have* you .... lived in another country?	a) .... we were both seven years old.
2 What was it .... ?	b) Yes, I .... I lived in Germany for two years.
3 How .... have you known your best friend?	c) Oh, yes, we argue .... the time!
4 .... you ever disagreed about anything?	d) It .... fine. But I missed my friends here.

1 ....   2 ....   3 ....   4 ....

Move on

10 Read what Damian says. Then complete the conversation.

Hi, I'm Damian. I'm 16. I'm from Romania. I live in Brasov, where I was born. It's a nice place. It's about a two-hour drive north of the capital, Bucharest.

For a long time, my parents have wanted to move to Bucharest, but I like living here. All my friends are here. And you can go skiing, too, in the mountains. I've just been. It was great. It was my second holiday this year. I went to the Black Sea coast in the summer.

Next year, I'm hoping to go with my friends on a tour of Europe.

You: What's Brasov like, Damian?

Damian: *It's a nice place.* ....

You: ¹ .... ?

Damian: Since I was born.

You: ² ....
             .... ?

Damian: My parents have, but I haven't,
             because ³ ....
             and ⁴ ....

You: ⁵ .... ?

Damian: Yes, I do. I go quite a lot. There's a
             ski resort just outside Brasov.

You: ⁶ .... ?

Damian: It's great.

You: ⁷ ....
             .... ?

Damian: Yes, I have. I went last summer.

You: ⁸ ....
             .... ?

Damian: No, never, but I'm hoping to go on
             one next year.

Go for it

11 In your notebook, write your answers to these questions.

1 How long have you known your best friend?

2 Have you ever disagreed about anything? Give details.

3 Has your friend ever been annoyed with you? Give details.

Boost your Writing 2

Dialogue

1 Complete the conversation.

Laura: Hello. We haven't met. I'm Laura Barton, the Director of Studies.

Kasia: Hello, I'm Kasia Lukic.

Laura: _How long_ have you been here, Kasia?

Kasia: Since Monday.

Laura: And ¹..................................... things?

Kasia: Fine, ²................ .

Laura: What's your accommodation ³........ ?

Kasia: It's fine.

Laura: Is it close to the school?

Kasia: It's about 10km away, so it takes about an hour to get here.

Laura: Really?

Kasia: Yes, I'm going to look for a place which is closer.

Laura: Maybe I can help. ⁴............. a coffee?

Kasia: Yes, if ⁵................ all right. Are you sure you've got time?

Laura: Yes, ⁶................ course. I've got the next hour free, so it's fine.

2 In your notebook, write a similar conversation between you and Jack, an English student who's on an exchange visit to your school. Include all the numbered phrases from Exercise 1.

- Jack arrived last Saturday
- The family he's staying with live a long way from the school.
- You've got the next lesson free.

Text: Write a travel article

3 Read Jack's article and number the topics in the correct order.

Cities	☐
Seasons	☐
Transport	☐
Most popular places in London	☐
Accommodation	☐
Best time to visit	☐
Countryside	1
Personal favourites	☐

A VISITOR'S GUIDE TO THE UK

If you visit the UK, try to see some of the beautiful countryside. You'll be surprised at the variety. Visit the Lake District in the north-west of England, take a boat out to the Farne Islands in the north-east, walk along the dramatic Cornish coast in the south-west, or climb the mountains of Scotland and Wales.

As well as the countryside, you should visit big cities like London and Edinburgh. Lots of people go to the big attractions, like Buckingham Palace, Madame Tussaud's and the London Eye. The views from the top of the Eye are fantastic. But I also make sure visitors see other places that I really like, such as Stratford-on-Avon and Bath.

There are trains and buses to most places, so it isn't difficult to travel around the UK. And you can usually find a place to stay. 'B&Bs' are popular – 'B&B' stands for 'bed and breakfast'.

Winters in the UK are cold, and the days are short. Summers are warm, but it sometimes rains for long periods. In my opinion, spring is the best time, because I like being out in the fresh air. But whenever you come, I'm sure you'll enjoy yourself!

4 Underline the following words and phrases in Jack's article. Then use them to complete the sentences below.

> • as well as • also • or • so • in my opinion

It's nearly summer __so__ book your holiday now!

1 It's important to visit the north .... the south of the country.

2 You can either go by bus .... by train.

3 .... , you should spend your first week in London.

4 You can go over the bridge, but there's .... a ferry service.

5 Use the above ideas and Jack's article to write a visitor's guide to your country in your notebook. Try to include the words and phrases in Exercise 4.

Reading

The most famous teenagers on Earth

Mary-Kate and Ashley were born on 13th June 1986. Ashley, born two minutes before Mary-Kate, is more talkative.

They appear in films and they are on TV in shows like *So Little Time* and *Two of a Kind*. They sing, they dance, they write, they design clothes, they have their own magazine and website, and they are worth a fortune. It's possible that you have never heard of Mary-Kate and Ashley Olsen. But it's unlikely, because the Olsen twins are the hottest thing around. In fact, they're the most successful teenagers in the USA. Last year, sales of their magazines, videos and clothes exceeded $500 million.

Interviewer:	Have you always been interested in clothes?
Ashley:	We've loved fashion ever since we can remember.
Interviewer:	When did you first appear on TV?
Mary-Kate:	We've been in front of the camera since we were nine months old!
Interviewer:	What's the best thing about being famous?
Ashley:	Travelling to other parts of the world.
Interviewer:	Have you travelled a lot?
Ashley:	Recently, we've been to Australia, England, France and Italy.
Interviewer:	Do you ever pretend to be one another?
Mary-Kate:	People ask us that question all the time. No, we have never switched places.
Interviewer:	Have you ever fought over boys?
Ashley:	We've never had a big fight, but we like the same types, it's true!
Interviewer:	What was the coolest place you visited in Britain?
Mary-Kate:	It's hard to pick just one place. But the shopping is great!

Comprehension

Stay cool

1 Complete the chart.

Names	*Mary-Kate* and .... Olsen	
Family relationship	....	
Date of birth	....	
Nationality	....	
Skills	*Singing*............., ..., ..., ...	
Countries visited	....................., ..., ..., ...	

Move on

2 Answer the questions.

Where do Mary-Kate and Ashley live?

In the USA.
....

1 Who is older, Mary-Kate or Ashley?

....

2 Have they always liked clothes?

....

3 What did they do when they were nine months old?

....

4 Why are boyfriends sometimes a problem?

....

5 What did they like about Britain?

....

Go for it

3 Use the information in the text to complete these sentences.

Sales of their books, videos and clothes exceeded $500 million, so *they are worth a fortune.*

1 Mary-Kate isn't as ....

2 They've always ....

3 Travelling is ....

....

4 They can't say which was the coolest place in Britain because ....

....

Communication

4 Write the questions in this conversation.

A: *Have you ever heard of the Olsen twins?*.....

B: Of course I have. Everybody's heard of them!

A: ¹.. ?

B: They're OK, I suppose. They're very rich! And nothing gets in their way.

A: ².. ?

B: Well, they do a bit of everything. And they're on TV.

A: ³.. ?

B: Yes, I have. They were in a show called *So Little Time.*

A: ⁴.. ?

B: Yes, since they were very young.

A: ⁵.. ?

B: Yes, they have. They liked the shops!

Writing

5 You've heard that Mary-Kate and Ashley (or other famous people) are visiting your city. Write them an informal letter in your notebook. You'd like to invite them to come to your school to talk about their work and their travels ...

- Start by saying why you are writing.

- Say why you're inviting them ('to talk to us about...').

- Add a suitable ending.

6 They were exploring the glacier.

Vocabulary

Stay cool

1 Find seven more verbs of movement.

L	O	U	S	T	S
G	F	D	T	E	I
S	A	P	R	U	N
J	L	M	U	T	K
U	L	W	G	S	O
M	P	C	G	W	V
P	O	S	L	I	P
D	I	V	E	M	L

jump ....

1 ....
2 ....
3 ....
4 ....
5 ....
6 ....
7 ....

Move on

2 Complete the sentences. Use each of the verbs in Exercise 1 once only.

One metre isn't high. You can easily
jump .... over that.

1 Come on, ... ! We're going to miss the bus.

2 You mustn't .... from those rocks. The water isn't deep enough.

3 Don't go near the edge of the cliff. You don't want to .... off!

4 The roads are icy. Don't .... !

5 Don't .... with all those bags. I'll help you.

6 Can you .... under water?

7 Don't worry. The boat isn't going to .... !

Go for it

3 Write what the penguins are saying in each picture. Include a verb of movement in each.

My boat *sank!* ....

1 It's not far! Just .... !

2 You're going to learn to ....

3 Come on, ... in!

4 You're quite safe. Don't ....

Grammar

Stay cool

Past simple and past continuous

4 Match the questions and the answers.

1 What did you do after the match?
2 Why didn't you answer the phone?

3 What was the party like?
4 Why did you leave the party early?

5 Where were Sasha and Eva on Saturday morning?
6 What did Sasha and Eva do on Saturday morning?

7 Did Edward get anything for Chloe on her birthday?
8 Was Edward on his way to Chloe's house?

9 Where was Annabel yesterday?
10 What was the best bit about Annabel's holiday?

11 What happened when you switched the TV on?
12 What was wrong with your TV?

a) Yes, he was taking her some flowers.
b) Yes, he took her some flowers.

c) They were doing the shopping.
d) They did the shopping.

e) She learned to windsurf.
f) She was learning to windsurf.

g) I was having a shower
h) I had a shower.

i) It was making a funny noise.
j) It made a funny noise.

k) We weren't enjoying it.
l) We didn't enjoy it.

1 _h_   3 ....   5 ....   7 ....   9 ....   11 ....

2 ....   4 ....   6 ....   8 ....   10 ....   12 ....

Prepositions of motion

5 Write the prepositions of motion.

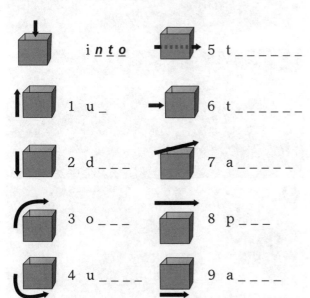

i _n t o_   5 t _ _ _ _ _ _

1 u _   6 t _ _ _ _ _ _

2 d _ _ _   7 a _ _ _ _ _

3 o _ _ _   8 p _ _ _

4 u _ _ _ _   9 a _ _ _ _

Move on

Past simple and continuous

6 Complete the sentences by putting one verb into the past simple and one into the past continuous.

(you / throw) **_Did you throw_** my magazines out when you (tidy) **_were tidying_** up?

1 We (find) .... an old coin when we (explore) .... the coast.

2 You (cut) .... your foot because you (not wear) .... shoes.

3 Who (you / wait) .... for when I (see) .... you?

4 While they (choose) .... music for the party, the CD player (go) .... wrong.

5 (you / remember) .... to invite Sara to the party when you (speak) .... to her?

6 I (not hear) .... you because I (do) .... the vacuuming.

6

7 Complete the article using the past simple or past continuous of the verbs in brackets.

Brave Zoe (16) swims out to rescue horse

A teenage horse lover nearly (drown) **drowned** yesterday after she (dive) [1]...................... into the freezing sea to rescue a runaway horse.

Zoe Kerry, 16, (walk) [2].................................. along Dovey Beach in South Wales with some friends and their horses. Suddenly, one of the horses, Ben, (escape) [3]......................... and (run) [4]......................... into the sea.

'My friend Becky (go) [5]..................... after him,' said Zoe, 'but when I (get) [6]..................... there, he (swim) [7]..................... around in the sea.'

Zoe (throw off) [8]..................... her coat and shoes and (swim) [9]..................... out to help Ben. Becky (call) [10]..................... the coastguards. They (arrive) [11]..................... within minutes, but the sea (push) [12]..................... Zoe further along the coast. The coastguards (pull) [13]..................... Ben to safety, but Zoe (still / struggle) [14]..................... .... against the waves.

'I (swim) [15]..................... for three or four minutes and finally (manage) [16]..................... to climb onto a sandbank,' said Zoe. She (wait) [17]..................... 20 minutes for a lifeboat to rescue her. An ambulance then (take) [18]..................... her to hospital, where she (recover) [19]..................... last night from hypothermia.

'I know it was a silly thing to do,' said Zoe, 'but Ben (drown) [20].................................. in front of my eyes.'

when, while

8 Join these pairs of sentences to make one new sentence. Write the new sentences in your notebook.

1 Zoe and her friends were walking with their horses. One of the horses escaped.

   a) Use *when*

   Zoe and her friends were walking with their horses when one of the horses escaped.

   b) Use *while*

2 The coastguards arrived. Zoe was trying to reach Ben.

   a) Use *when*   b) Use *while*

Go for it

Past simple and continuous
Time markers *while, as, when*
Prepositions of motion

9 Look at the pictures below. Then in your notebook, write about what happened to Laura Brown. Include the words in the box.

> **nouns**
> • rucksack • path • rocks
> • thunderstorm • ankle • helicopter
> • stretcher • hospital
>
> **verbs (past simple or continuous)**
> • to pack • to fall over • to break
> • to wave • to land • to dial 999
>
> **time markers**
> • while • as • when
>
> **prepositions of motion**

It was a beautiful day, so Laura Brown decided to ...

26

Stay cool

10 Look at the map. You have just finished playing crazy golf at the Putting Green and you have decided to walk to Beacon Cove. Complete the directions.

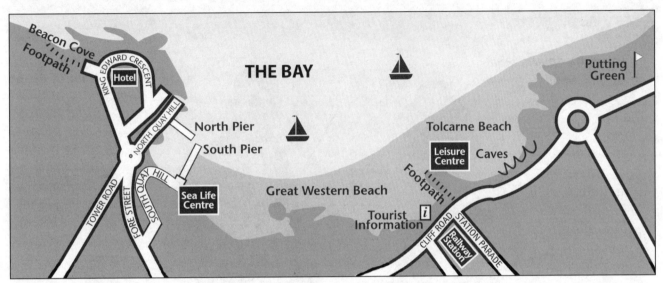

• past   • along
• up   • ~~down~~
• from   • down
• until you get to
• turn right into
• turn left

The quickest way to Beacon Cove is to go _down_ to Tolcarne Beach. Then walk [1].. the beach. Go [2]..............................
.... the caves and keep walking [3]..
the South Pier. Go [4].. South Quay Hill and
[5].. Fore Street. When you get to the roundabout, go straight on. You'll see a big hotel in front of you.
[6].. at the hotel. There's a footpath
[7].. the road [8].. to Beacon Cove.

Move on / Go for it

11 A tourist asks you for directions from the hotel to South Pier. Write the conversation.

Tourist: *Excuse me, could you* ....
....
....

You: ....
....
....
....
....
....
....
....

What's wrong?

12 Circle and correct the mistakes.

Take the first turning on◯right.
Take the first turning on the right. ....

1 Could you tell me where is the post office?
....

2 I've lost my sunglasses, and I wore them a moment ago.
....

3 Let's go passed the cinema to see what's on.
....

4 I swum across the bay yesterday.
....

7 I've just spilt coffee.

Vocabulary

Stay cool

1 Label the clothes 1–8.

Move on

2 Add these labels to the photo of the boy.

- sleeve
- collar
- turn-ups
- cuff
- laces
- pocket

3 Complete the sentences using the words and phrases.

- situation comedy • jokes • cartoon • romantic comedy
- sense of humour • ~~slapstick~~ • stand-up comedian • spoof

I know it's only *slapstick*, but I still laugh when I see somebody slip on a banana skin.

1 He's got a good ....
He makes me laugh.

2 I never laugh at his ....
I just don't find them funny.

3 It's a funny film, and there's a love story, so I suppose it's a ....

4 *Friends* is on every week from 10 to 10.30.
It's a ....

5 She performs at The Bridge Café every Friday night. She's a ....
....

6 Which *Batman* film do you prefer – the version with real actors or the
.... ?

7 You think it's a serious programme to begin with, and then you realise it's a
....

Go for it

4 Complete the description of what this man is wearing.

The 1960s

He's wearing a striped ...*shirt*... .

It's got long [1].......... and a [2].......... with buttons.

He's also wearing a spotted [3].......... .

Around his waist, there's a wide [4].......... .

His [5].......... are wide at the bottom with big [6].......... .

Grammar

Stay cool

Question tags

5 Complete the sentences with the correct question tags.

Your aunt's the manager of the hotel, ...*isn't she*... ?

1 You don't work at the hotel, ... ?

2 I'm not late, ... ?

3 You're here for the championships,

.... ?

4 Tom doesn't live in London, ... ?

5 You and Louise went to town, ...

.... ?

6 Your journey wasn't very good, ... ?

7 We were standing at the same bus stop,

.... ?

8 You've both been to St Ives before,

.... ?

9 You aren't working late, ... ?

10 They weren't at the beach, ... ?

Past simple and present perfect simple

6 Circle the letter of the correct response.

Do you like London?

a) I didn't go there.

(b) I haven't been there.

1 Where were you last night?

a) I was at Laura's.

b) I've been at Laura's.

2 Let's go to the new shopping centre.

a) I already went.

b) I've already been.

3 What was your skiing holiday like?

a) It was great.

b) It's been great.

4 What was that noise?

a) I didn't hear anything.

b) I haven't heard anything

5 You can use the computer now.

a) Did you finish?

b) Have you finished?

6 I like your new jacket.

a) I wore it every day this week.

b) I've worn it every day this week.

7 Have you ever eaten Indian food?

a) Yes, I tried it when I was in London.

b) Yes, I've tried it when I was in London.

Move on

Past simple and present perfect simple

just, already, yet

7 Complete Rachel's letter to her brother at university. Use the past simple or the present perfect simple of the verbs in brackets.

Dear Rob

(I / just / spend) **I've just spent** two hours at a birthday party with 20 screaming five-year-olds!

(I / just / start) ¹.. a part-time job as a party assistant at the leisure centre. (They / want) ².. someone who was good at sport and good with children. Believe it or not, (I / get) ³................. the job.

(It / be) ⁴.............. only my second party, and (I / already / have) ⁵.. enough! (The first party / not be) ⁶.. too bad because (we / play) ⁷........................ party games. But today was different. (One little boy / try) ⁸......................... to climb a ladder in the gym and (fall) ⁹.............. off. (A little girl / jump) ¹⁰......................... off the trampoline and (land) ¹¹......................... on me. I know it was only for two hours, but (I / never / work) ¹².. so hard in my whole life! (I / not give up) ¹³.. the job yet, but I'm close!

How are things with you? (you / have) ¹⁴.. any job interviews yet? Not surprisingly, (I / already / decide) ¹⁵.. that I'd rather teach in a secondary school than a primary school!

Write soon

Love

Rachel

Go for it

Present perfect simple with *just, already, yet*

8 Give suitable reasons, using *just*, *already* and *yet* with the present perfect.

just

		Reason
	I'm afraid Charlotte's not here.	She *'s just gone out.*...........................
1	I don't want a sandwich, thanks.	I ....
2	We haven't met our neighbours yet.	We ....
3	I'm not going to the shop again.	I ....

already

4	They don't want to go and see the new Julia Roberts film.	They ....
5	You don't need to take the rubbish out.	I ....
6	I won't phone Mark about the party.	Sarah ....

yet

7	Max doesn't know that Susie's moving to Cornwall.	She ....
8	I don't know the new leisure centre.	I ....
9	You say you don't like my special curry, but how do you know?	You ....

Communication

Stay cool

9 Use the information in the chart to complete the conversation with Martín.

Name	Martín Alejandro Ricca Peirone
Age	18
Home	(since 1998) Mexico
Country of birth	Argentina
First record	*Broken Hearts* (recorded 1998)

You: Martín, can I just check some details?

Martín: Yes, of course.

You: Your full name is Martín Alejandro Ricca Peirone, ***isn't it?*** ....

Martín: Yes, it is.

You: And you were born in Argentina,
¹.................................... ?

Martín: That's right, I was.

You: And you're 18, ²........................... ?

Martín: Yes, I am.

You: You've lived in Mexico since 1998,
³............................... ?

Martín: That's right.

You: And your first record was *Broken Hearts*, ⁴....................... ?

Martín: Yes, I recorded it in 1998.

Move on

10 Complete the questions from this interview with Martín. Use question tags.

I = Interviewer   M = Martín

I: *You're from San Luis, aren't you?*
....

M: Well, yes, I'm from San Luis, but I lived in Córdoba until I was 12.

1 **I:** ....
.... ?

M: Yes, it's true, I like all kinds of music. In Spanish, I like Alejandro Sanz and Luis Miguel. In English, I like Pink Floyd and the Rolling Stones.

2 **I:** ....
.... ?

M: Yes, I'd like to record in English. But not yet. I'm going to learn English first!

3 **I:** ....
.... ?

M: Yes, Mexico has been very important for my career. It began here.

4 **I:** ....
.... ?

M: Yes, I'm planning to visit other countries. I really want to go to the USA and Spain.

Go for it

11 Check three more pieces of information about Martín. You've heard that ...

- he's got a dog called Puppy;
- he likes playing football in his free time;
- he's working on a new album;
- he's going to write some songs for his new album.

You've got a dog called Puppy, haven't you?
....

1 ....
....

2 ....
....

3 ....
....

Boost your Writing 3

1 Use the verbs in brackets in the correct tense (past simple or past continuous) to complete the story.

I (be) _was_ only eight years old at the time. Mum and I (walk) _were walking_ through the fields. We (play) ¹........................ with a ball. I threw the ball to my mum, but she (not catch) ²........................ it. It (go) ³.................... into the water. As Mum (try) ⁴........................ to get the ball, the edge of the river bank (give way) ⁵........................ and she (fall in) ⁶........................ . My mum can't swim!

While she (struggle) ⁷.................................... to reach the bank, I (manage) ⁸........................ to catch the collar of her jacket and I (pull) ⁹........................ her towards me. She (reach) ¹⁰........................ the edge, but as she (climb up) ¹¹.................................... the bank, she fell in again. Finally, she (get out) ¹².................... She was very wet. It was time to go home. We (walk) ¹³........................ home when I (start) ¹⁴........................ laughing.

I couldn't stop! My mum's got a good sense of humour, but she (not think) ¹⁵.................... .... it was funny.

2 Underline these words in the story. Then use them to combine the following sentences.

| • as • while • when |

  (as)   I was leaving the flat. I noticed that a window was open.

       As I was leaving the flat, I noticed
       that a window was open.

1 (as)   A fox ran out in front of us. We were cycling along the lane.

       ....
       ....

2 (while) You were doing the shopping. We made a cake.

       ....
       ....

3 (while) I read a magazine. I was waiting to see the doctor.

       ....
       ....

4 (when) We were winning 3–1. It started to rain.

       ....
       ....

5 (when) I was walking into town. I saw your cousins.

       ....
       ....

3 Either use the notes and pictures below to write a story or write a similar story of your own. Try to use *as*, *while* and *when*.

- my friend Charlie and I / climb a tree in the park

- he and I / talk
- he / slip

- he / fall
- he / catch a branch of the tree

- the branch / break
- Charlie / land on the ground

- I / really worried
- I / call for help
- Charlie / get up / start to laugh

I was only ten years old at the time. My friend Charlie and I were climbing a tree in the park. While ...

8 You ought to try them.

Vocabulary

Stay cool

1 Which of the cooking terms can go with each food item?

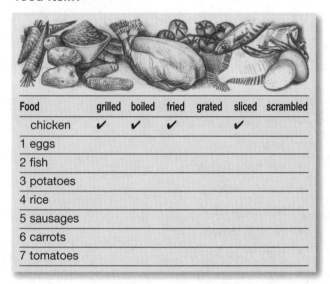

Food	grilled	boiled	fried	grated	sliced	scrambled
chicken	✔	✔	✔		✔	
1 eggs						
2 fish						
3 potatoes						
4 rice						
5 sausages						
6 carrots						
7 tomatoes						

Move on

2 Describe each item in two words.

b**aked** p**otatoes**   s.............. c...............

f............ e...............   ch............ o...............

g.............. c...............   g.............. ch.............

Go for it

3 Complete the questionnaire.

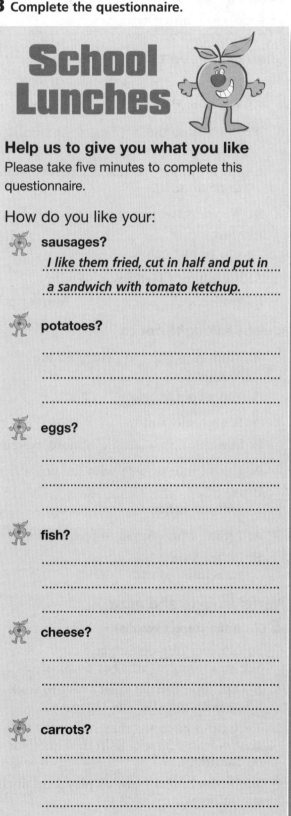

School Lunches

Help us to give you what you like
Please take five minutes to complete this questionnaire.

How do you like your:

sausages?
I like them fried, cut in half and put in a sandwich with tomato ketchup.

potatoes?
....
....
....

eggs?
....
....
....

fish?
....
....
....

cheese?
....
....
....

carrots?
....
....
....

Grammar

Stay cool

Verbs *should/shouldn't* and *ought to/ ought not to*

4 Give advice for these situations, using the verbs in the box.

> • do • give • ~~go~~ • ~~help~~ • ride
> • send • swim • walk

should/shouldn't

A: I'm always tired in the mornings.

B: You *should go* to bed earlier.

1 A: She missed the last bus, so she walked home.

B: She .... home alone at night.

2 A: We went swimming straight after lunch.

B: You .... when you've just eaten.

3 A: It's Oliver's birthday on Friday.

B: We .... him a card.

ought to/ought not to

A: Mum says she can't carry all the shopping.

B: You *ought to help* her.

4 A: She's really unfit.

B: She .... more exercise.

5 A: He got into trouble with the police.

B: He .... his bike without lights.

6 A: I think Mum forgot to feed the cat.

B: Perhaps we .... it something to eat.

Verbs *have to* and *must*

5 Circle the correct word(s).

She's never free on Sundays.
She *must* /(*has to*) visit her cousins.

1 It's OK. You *mustn't* / *don't have to* walk home with me after the cinema.

2 They can't go to the match because they always *must* / *have to* help their mother on Saturdays.

3 You *mustn't* / *don't have to* play loud music late at night.

4 *Must you* / *Do you have to* be at school by 8.30?

5 What jobs *must she* / *does she have to* do at home?

6 We've eaten a lot of pizza this week. We *must* / *have to* try to eat more fresh fruit.

Move on

Verbs *should/shouldn't* and *ought to/ ought not to*

6 Give two pieces of advice for each situation. The phrases below will help you.

- • drink so much coffee
- • eat sweets all the time
- • touch it
- • eat so quickly
- • go to the dentist
- • tell someone
- • turn it down
- • play it so loudly
- • try to relax more
- • have a glass of water

should/shouldn't

A: I get a lot of headaches.

B: *You should try to relax more.*
You shouldn't drink so much coffee.

1 A: She's got hiccups again.

B: She ....

She ....

2 A: My teeth hurt.

B: You ....

You ....

ought to/ought not to

3 A: There's a large bag by the check-in desk, but there's nobody with it.

B: We ....

We ....

4 A: The neighbours have complained about my music.

B: You ....

You ....

Go for it

Verbs *should* and *ought to*
Verbs *have to* and *must*

7 Complete the e-mails using the positive or negative
form of *should/ought to*, *have to* or *must*.

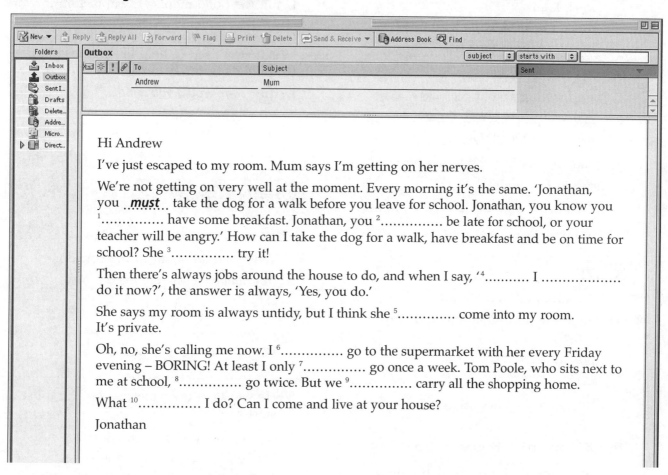

Hi Andrew

I've just escaped to my room. Mum says I'm getting on her nerves.

We're not getting on very well at the moment. Every morning it's the same. 'Jonathan, you ..**must**.. take the dog for a walk before you leave for school. Jonathan, you know you [1]............... have some breakfast. Jonathan, you [2]............... be late for school, or your teacher will be angry.' How can I take the dog for a walk, have breakfast and be on time for school? She [3]............... try it!

Then there's always jobs around the house to do, and when I say, '[4]........... I .... do it now?', the answer is always, 'Yes, you do.'

She says my room is always untidy, but I think she [5]............... come into my room. It's private.

Oh, no, she's calling me now. I [6]............... go to the supermarket with her every Friday evening – BORING! At least I only [7]............... go once a week. Tom Poole, who sits next to me at school, [8]............... go twice. But we [9]............... carry all the shopping home.

What [10]............... I do? Can I come and live at your house?

Jonathan

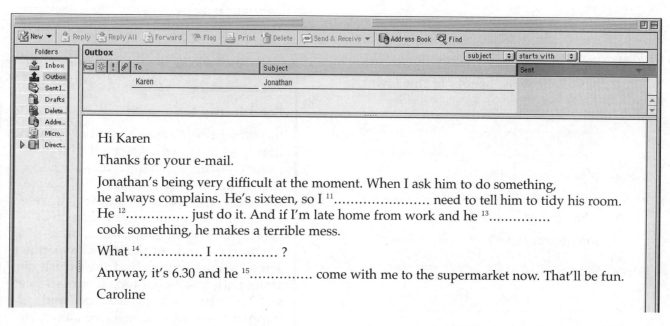

Hi Karen

Thanks for your e-mail.

Jonathan's being very difficult at the moment. When I ask him to do something, he always complains. He's sixteen, so I [11]........................ need to tell him to tidy his room. He [12]............... just do it. And if I'm late home from work and he [13]............... cook something, he makes a terrible mess.

What [14]............... I .... ?

Anyway, it's 6.30 and he [15]............... come with me to the supermarket now. That'll be fun.

Caroline

What advice would you give to Jonathan and/or his mum?

....

....

Stay cool

8 Use the prompts to complete the dialogues.

A: (fetch Vanessa from school?)

(work late)

Would you mind fetching Vanessa from school? I have to work late.

B: (✓) *No, not at all.*

(✗ a meeting at four o'clock)

Sorry, I'm afraid I can't. I've got a meeting at four o'clock.

1 **A:** (take my books back to the library?)

(sprain my ankle)

....

....

....

B: (✓)

....

2 **A:** (go to the post office on your way home?)

(post this letter today)

....

....

....

B: (✗ not go past the post office today)

....

....

....

3 **A:** (help me with my History homework?)

(write about the history of this town)

....

....

....

B: (✓)

....

4 **A:** (change a £50 note?)

(buy a bus ticket)

....

....

....

B: (✗ haven't got any change)

....

....

Move on / Go for it

9 In your notebook, write the conversation for this situation.

Lynn, the hotel manager, wants Tom to work late this evening because she has to go out. Unfortunately, Tom can't stay late because he has promised to help his mother prepare for Jamie's birthday party.

Lynn: *Tom, would you mind ... ?*

What's wrong?

10 Circle and correct the mistakes.

You should(nt) shout in the corridor.

You shouldn't shout in the corridor.

1 Can I give you hand?

....

2 Would you mind to pass me the salt?

....

3 He works at the supermarket. He must start at 7.30.

....

4 Do you like smashed potato?

....

CULTURE SNAPSHOT

Food in the UK

In many British towns and cities, you will find restaurants which serve Chinese, Indian, Japanese, Thai, Greek, Turkish, Italian, Spanish, Mexican and, of course, American-style food. Dishes which were once quite unusual in the UK, such as curry, pasta, paella, moussaka, pizza, hamburgers and kebabs, are now popular. They have become part of the British diet, along with traditional food like roast beef and Yorkshire pudding, sausages and mashed potatoes, and fish and chips.

Have any dishes from the UK become popular in your country?

9 They've been bullying me.

Vocabulary

Stay cool

1 Write a sentence for each picture using the adjectives in the box.

> • shy • nasty • happy • ~~lonely~~
> • nervous • jealous • miserable

He's lonely.

1 He's ....

2 She's ....

3 ....

4 ....

5 ....

6 ....

Move on

2 Write the adjectives from Exercise 1 and change them into nouns.

	lonely	*loneliness*
1	....	....
2	....	....
3	....	....
4	....	....
5	....	....
6	....	....

Go for it

3 Choose an adjective or a noun from Exercise 2 to complete these sentences.

That was a horrible thing to say! Why were you so *nasty* to her?

1 My grandmother lives alone, but she's got a lot of friends, so .... isn't a problem for her.

2 He has difficulty talking to people because he's so ....

3 Tara doesn't like Kate just because Kate's got blonde hair and blue eyes. .... is a terrible thing.

4 Don't be .... You'll feel better if you smile.

5 I always feel .... before playing in front of a lot of people.

6 It was the best time of my life, a time of great ....

9 Grammar

Stay cool

Present perfect continuous with *for* **and** *since*

4 Make sentences in the present perfect continuous using the prompts.

We / take things easy / two weeks

We've been taking things easy for two weeks.

1 I / save money / last July

....

....

2 He / look for his keys / hours

....

....

3 They / not talk to each other / ages

....

....

4 She / not sleep well / she had the car accident

....

....

5 you / try / to phone me ?

....

....

6 How long / they / work in California?

....

....

Move on

Present perfect continuous

5 Complete the sentences, using the present perfect continuous of the verbs in the box.

• do	• drive	• ~~expect~~	• explore
• live	• look for	• try	• save

A: Welcome, *I've been expecting* .... you.

B: How long [1] .... here?
A: Oh, for ages.

A: What [2] .... here in Transylvania?
C: We [3] .... the countryside.

A: Oh, here's Cerberus! I expect he [4] ....
.... food. He's always hungry.

38

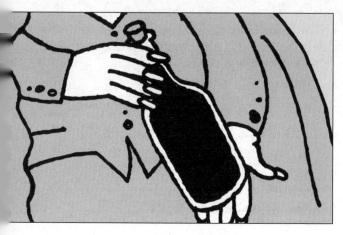

: Would you like to try some of this?
I ⁵.................................. it for a special evening.

: Oh, no, thanks. We're both feeling quite tired.

: Of course you're tired. You ⁶............................. all day. Would you like me to show you to your room?

: Quick! Let's go!

: Too late! Here he is now!

: I ⁷... to mend your car, but it's bad news, I'm afraid.

Go for it

Present perfect simple and continuous with *for* and *since*

6 Read the article and complete the interview, using the correct form of the verbs in brackets: present perfect simple or continuous.

I started ice-skating when I was 6, and then when I was 11 I decided to try ice hockey. When I was 14, I went to the national trials and got into the team. I was

Claire Oldfield, 17
Member of the British women's ice-hockey team at 14.

incredibly nervous at first, but the other players were really helpful.

My sport hasn't affected school. Matches are at the weekend, not on school days. Recently, we've been training four evenings a week, but I still have time for homework. My friends didn't really take any notice when I first started playing, but now I think they're really jealous of all the travelling I do!

You: Claire, how long (play) *have you been playing* ice hockey?

Claire: ¹...
....

You: And how long (be) ²...........................
.... in the national team?

Claire: ³...

You: (ever / miss) ⁴.......................................
.... school because of your sport?

Claire: ⁵...

You: (train) ⁶... a lot recently?

Claire: ⁷...
....

You: And what about your friends?

Claire: I think they're a bit jealous of all the travelling I do!

9 | Communication

Stay cool

7 Offer to help in these situations. Use the following expressions:

- Would you like me to ...? / Shall I ...?
  - go with you
  - (– phone for you)
  - carry them for you
  - record it for you
- Yes, please. That's very kind of you.
- No, don't worry. I'll be OK. / I can manage, thanks.

Your friend has to make a phone call to England, but she's shy about speaking English.

Would you like me to phone for you?

She accepts your offer.

Yes, please. That's very kind of you.

1 Your friend has to go out this evening, and there's a programme on TV which she really wants to see.

....

....

She accepts your offer.

....

....

2 Your friend has got two very heavy bags.

....

She refuses your offer.

....

....

3 Your friend has to go to the dentist's. He's nervous.

....

....

He refuses your offer.

....

....

Move on

8 A good friend is having a party. Use the prompts to write a conversation.

A: Offer to help with the food.

Would you like me to help with the food?
....

B: Refuse politely and give a reason.

¹ *No, ...*..

....

A: Offer to make some tapes.

²..

....

B: Accept the offer.

³..

A: Ask what time the party starts.

⁴..

B: Respond.

⁵..

A: Offer to come earlier and give a reason.

⁶..

....

B: Accept the offer.

⁷..

Go for it

9 Your friend Rick needs help. In your notebook, write a conversation.

Rick's problem ...

Last week I lent my dad's mobile phone to Kevin, a guy in my class. Now he won't give the phone back. For the last few days, Dad has been asking for the phone and I've been making different excuses. Kevin's been using the phone a lot and I know he's been making long-distance calls. He says I'll be in trouble if I tell my dad.

You: *You look fed up, Rick. What's the problem?*

Rick: *You know that guy Kevin at school? Well, I lent him my dad's mobile phone last week and ...*

Boost your Writing 4

Text: Write some advice

1 Read the following problem and answer from a teenage website and underline the different ways of giving advice.

Schools.net

I've just started at a new school. I've been here for two months, but I've been finding it difficult to make friends. What can I do? I was happy at my other school. I had a lot of friends there.

Megan

It's sometimes hard to make friends when you go to a new school. Why don't you join an after-school club to meet students with similar interests? And perhaps you could invite some of them to your house after school one day.

2 Give advice to people in these situations, using the following phrases.

- You really ought to ...
- Perhaps you could ...
- Why don't you ...?
- You must ...
- You should ...

Sometimes I can't see the blackboard in class. I've also been getting a lot of headaches recently. (go)
You should go to the doctor / have an eye test.

1 There's a girl in my class who lives on a farm. She says she's lonely. (invite)

....

....

2 Some boys at school have been bullying my little brother. (tell)

....

....

3 I'd like to go to a language school in England, but I don't know how to find out about courses. (ask)

....

....

4 My friend borrowed some money from me, but I think she's forgotten about it. (remind)

....

....

5 My friend has been late for school a lot recently. I'm worried that she's going to get into trouble with her teacher. (talk)

....

....

At my school, the other students have been making jokes about a new student. She's from the north of England and my school is in the south, so her accent's different. I think she's quite miserable.

Paige

My little sister has just started to wear glasses. She's got short hair. The other children in her class call her Harry Potter. She's quite shy. It really upsets her. It upsets me, too.

Ross

3 Read the problems above, then, in your notebook, write some advice to help these people. Use phrases from Exercise 2, the suggestions in the box below and any suggestions of your own.

- change the way she speaks
- talk to her teachers
- make fun of them
- sort them out
- invite her classmates to her house
- ask them why they are nasty to her
- make friends with students from another class

Reading

We were playing baseball at midnight

Laura Paterson has just been on a trip of a lifetime. On the last day of her trip, she wrote an account of her experience.

1 It's as big as England, France, Italy and Spain. It's the largest state in the U.S.A. It's Alaska!

2 I've been here since March. For the past three months, I've been living in a log cabin with the Kolvig family. They've got one son, Adam.

3 I've been going to school by sea plane with Adam. It's the only way to travel! A car is impractical, because 75% of the country is impossible to get to by road.

4 At school, we've been learning how to protect ourselves from brown bears. I hope I don't meet one!

5 Sled-dog racing is very popular here. In March, thousands of people came to watch the Iditarod, a 1,500-kilometre race across the snowy landscape.

6 I've been eating a lot of fish. Last weekend, we caught and baked a salmon over a beach fire. It was delicious.

7 I also took a sea kayak out with Adam.

8 And last night we were playing baseball at midnight, because the summer days are so long. It's paradise!

ALASKA FACT FILE

- The state capital is Juneau, but the biggest city is Anchorage, where nearly half the population lives.

- It's got 5,000 glaciers and 555,000 people.

- Of the 20 highest mountains in the USA, 17 are in Alaska.

- There are thousands of rivers and lakes in Alaska.

- There are more than 70 active volcanoes.

Comprehension

Stay cool

1 Match the paragraphs to the pictures.

1 _e)_   a)
2 ....
3 ....
4 ....
5 ....
6 ....
7 ....
8 ....

b)
c)

d)

e)

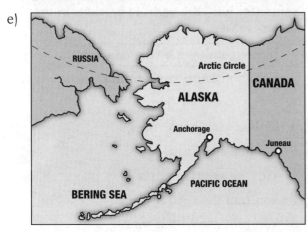

f)

g)

h)

Move on

2 **Find the names of ...**

a capital city   *Juneau* ....

1 a type of fish   ....

2 a large animal   ....

3 three means of   ....

transport   ....

     ....

4 five features of the   ....

landscape   ....

     ....

     ....

     ....

5 two sports   ....

     ....

Go for it

3 **Answer the questions.**

Which is bigger, Juneau or Anchorage?

Anchorage ....

1 About how many people live in
Anchorage? ....

2 Which month is it when Laura writes her
account? ....

3 Laura watched sled-dog racing and ate
salmon on the beach. Which did she do
first? ....

4 What's special about summer in Alaska?

....

Writing

4 **In your notebook, write a paragraph about
Laura's stay in Alaska. Note down the answers
to these questions first.**

- When did she go?
- How long did she go for?
- Where did she stay?
- What did she do during the week?
- What did she do in her free time?
- What did she do on her last night?

11 Unless I get to bed, ...

Grammar

Stay cool

Verbs *will/won't*, *might/might not* for predictions

1 Complete the conversation using *will/won't* or *might/might not*.

Liam: Have you got any plans for the summer?

Kim: Well, we haven't decided yet, but we _might_ go camping in New Zealand.

Liam: Camping in New Zealand in July? The weather [1].................... be awful! You can be sure it [2]........................ be cold and wet the whole time.

Danny: It was only an idea. Anyway, we [3]....................... have enough money to do it.

Liam: Why don't you go round Europe? I'm sure it [4]........................... be as expensive as a trip to New Zealand.

Kim: You [5]................................ be right.

Liam: I think you [6]................ have a great time. In fact, I was wondering about doing it myself.

Danny: Do you want to come with us?

Liam: I'd love to! I've got friends in Spain and Portugal. I can e-mail them. We [7]... be able to stay with them.

Kim: Sounds great!

First conditional: *if/unless* clause + *'ll (will)/won't*

2 Match the sentence halves. Then write the sentences with the verbs in brackets in the correct tense.

1. If we (go) down to the beach,
2. You (not want) your dinner
3. If the food (be) spicy,
4. Unless you (book) now,
5. We (have) a barbecue
6. We (not wait) for him
7. You (not pass) your exam
8. You (not catch) the train

a) she (not eat) it.
b) unless you (study).
c) if he (not be) here by six thirty.
d) if the weather (be) fine.
e) we (see) Matt.
f) if you (eat) all those chocolates.
g) unless you (leave) now.
h) you (not get) a ticket.

1 [e] *If we go down to the beach, we'll see Matt.*

2 [ ] ....
....

3 [ ] ....
....

4 [ ] ....
....

5 [ ] ....
....

6 [ ] ....
....

7 [ ] ....
....

8 [ ] ....
....

Move on

First conditional: *if/unless* clause + *'ll (will)/won't* or *may/may not*

3 Use the prompts to complete the exam advice.

✓ have short breaks while you are revising
✓ feel more relaxed

✓ work with loud music in the background
✗ be able to concentrate

✓ have the window open
? work better

1 ✓ make a revision timetable
✗ feel stressed

2 ✓ do some physical exercise
✓ feel better

3 ✓ work with soft music in the background
? be able to concentrate better

4 ✗ leave enough time for revision
? do your best in the exam

5 ✗ get enough sleep
✗ feel like working

Exam advice

If you have short breaks while you are revising, you'll feel more relaxed.

If you work with loud music in the background, you won't be able to concentrate.

If you have the window open, you may work better.

1 ....
....

2 ....
....

3 ....
....

4 ....
....

5 ....
....

Go for it

First conditional: *if/unless* clause + *'ll (will)*, *may* or *might*

4 What does Mark's mum say to him?

She thinks: He must be back home early. Otherwise, no supper!
She says: (*unless*) There ___*won't be any supper*___
___*unless you're back home early!*___

She thinks: He eats a lot of fatty foods. You can get spots from eating fatty foods.
She says: (*if*) You ___*might get spots if you eat*___
___*a lot of fatty foods.*___

1 She thinks: He never listens. So, of course, he never learns anything.
She says: (*unless*) You ....
....
....

2 She thinks: He's often late for school. Teachers sometimes give extra homework to students who are late.
She says: (*if*) Your teacher ....
....
....

3 She thinks: He will only get pocket money if he tidies his room.
She says: (*unless*) You ....
....
....

4 She thinks: I promise not to get angry, but he must get up before nine on Saturday.
She says: (*if*) I ....
....
....

Stay cool

5 Label the drawing.

> • arm • leg • eye • foot • ~~hair~~
> • hand • knee • toe • elbow
> • back • mouth • nose • shoulder

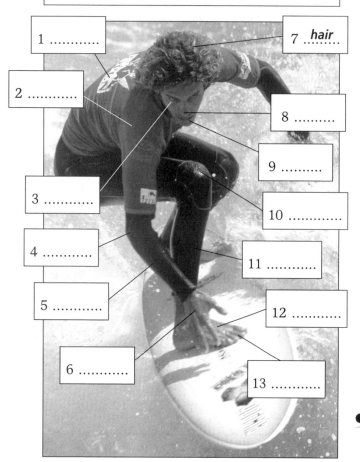

1 ....
2 ....
3 ....
4 ....
5 ....
6 ....
7 *hair*
8 ....
9 ....
10 ....
11 ....
12 ....
13 ....

6 You're e-mailing your friend. Write questions using *get*. You want to know …

if she received your last e-mail.

Did you get my last e-mail?

1 if she arrived at the leisure centre on time.

....

2 if she was nervous before her exam today.

....

....

3 if her friends were jealous when they saw her new jacket.

....

....

4 if she bought *Smash Hits* today.

....

5 if her brother found a place at university.

....

Move on

7 Complete the sentences using the correct form of *get* and the words in the box.

> • bored • crowded • excited • spots
> • serious • ~~upset~~ • wet • tips

Come on, Tania, dry your eyes.
Don't **get upset** . Forget about him.

1 We're going on holiday next week.
I .... so .... !

2 It's just started to rain. If you go out now, you ....

3 Listen, Harry, I like hanging out with you, but I don't want our relationship to
....

4 It's hard to keep my little brother interested in anything. He .... very easily.

5 A lot of people go there on Friday night. It .... very ....

6 If you eat a lot of fatty foods, you ....
....

7 When you worked as a waitress at The Pizza Place, ... you
.... good .... ?

Go for it

8 Use expressions with *get* to answer these questions.

1 What were your marks/grades in your last English test like?

I got ....
....

2 What sort of things make you angry?

....
....

3 Do you ever buy magazines?

....
....

4 Do you ever have headaches? If you do, what causes them?

....
....

5 How much sleep do you usually have?

....
....

Stay cool

9 Fill in the missing words to make negative questions.

1 *Aren't* you going on holiday with your parents this year?

2 .... you go into town last Saturday?

3 .... you seen the new Brad Pitt film yet?

4 .... you visit Disneyland when you go to Florida next summer?

5 .... you been to the Rock Garden Café?

6 .... you got a digital camera?

7 .... you like listening to music while you're doing your homework?

8 .... you going to continue learning the guitar?

Move on

10 Choose a reply for each question in Exercise 9.

Replies

a) No, I've lost interest in it.

b) No, I haven't. Where's it on?

c) No, I can't concentrate properly.

d) No, I had to help in the house.

e) No, I'm going on a cycling holiday with some schoolfriends.

f) No, but I'm going to get one soon.

g) No. There's not much for vegetarians there.

h) No, I went there two years ago.

1 *e)*   2 .....   3 .....   4 .....
5 .....   6 .....   7 .....   8 .....

Go for it

11 Use negative questions with the verbs in the box to show surprise in these situations.

- bring • ~~get~~ • have • open • want
- have got

Aren't you getting .... tired?

1 .... any Shakira CDs?

2 .... to dance?

3 .... any pizza?

4 .... your present?

5 .... a present?

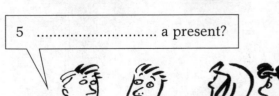

Vocabulary

Stay cool

1 **Match the adjectives to the pictures.**

- stupid • rude • unkind • ~~helpful~~
- kind

A: ... and the museum's on the right.

B: Thanks. You've been very _helpful_ .

1 **A:** Shut up!

   B: Sam! Don't be .... to your sister!

2 **A:** Would you like to sit down?

   B: That's very .... of you.

3 **A:** You've got spots.

   B: Don't be ....

4 I tried to get on the bus when it was
   moving. It was a .... thing to do.

Move on

2 **Circle ten more adjectives in the word square.**

K	Y	T	E	S	H	Y	E
R	C	P	O	E	L	E	Z
O	N	O	M	N	I	J	Y
L	E	L	A	S	R	E	R
C	R	I	T	I	C	A	L
T	V	T	U	B	N	L	H
U	O	E	R	L	K	O	A
R	U	D	E	E	I	U	P
E	S	P	F	W	N	S	P
F	R	I	E	N	D	L	Y

Go for it

3 **Describe someone who ...**

gets on well with other people.
friendly
....

1 never does stupid things.
....

2 never says 'please' or 'thank you'.
....

3 is angry when someone has something
   which they want.
....

4 likes examining things carefully.
....

5 likes doing things for other people.
....

Grammar

Stay cool / Move on

Present and past simple passive

4 Complete the information using the verbs in the present or past simple passive.

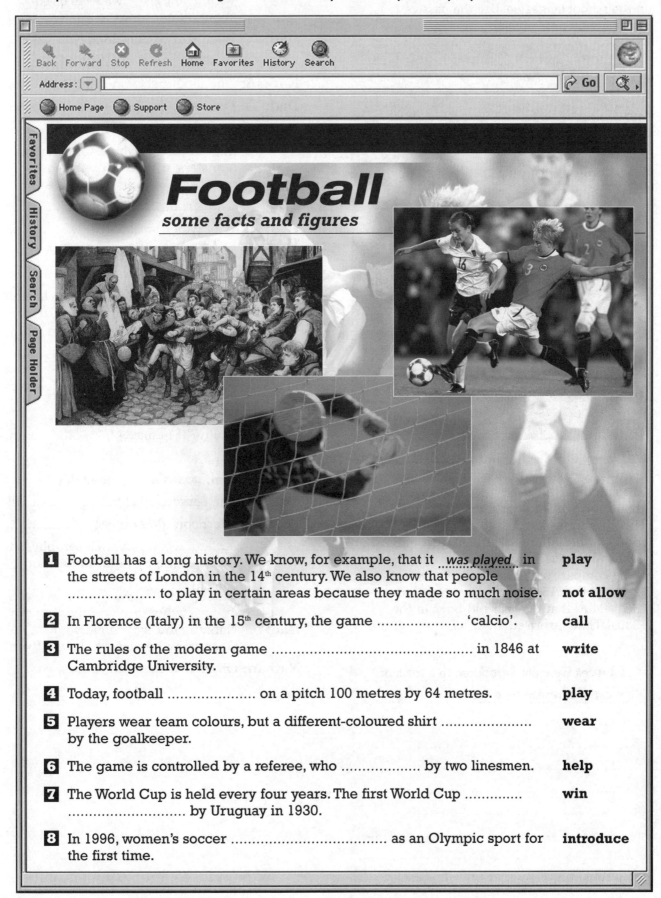

Football
some facts and figures

1 Football has a long history. We know, for example, that it _was played_ in **play**
the streets of London in the 14th century. We also know that people
.... to play in certain areas because they made so much noise. **not allow**

2 In Florence (Italy) in the 15th century, the game .... 'calcio'. **call**

3 The rules of the modern game .... in 1846 at **write**
Cambridge University.

4 Today, football .... on a pitch 100 metres by 64 metres. **play**

5 Players wear team colours, but a different-coloured shirt .... **wear**
by the goalkeeper.

6 The game is controlled by a referee, who .... by two linesmen. **help**

7 The World Cup is held every four years. The first World Cup .... **win**
.... by Uruguay in 1930.

8 In 1996, women's soccer .... as an Olympic sport for **introduce**
the first time.

Go for it

Present and past simple, active and passive

5 Rewrite what Nathan says for an article in the school magazine. Use the passive (present and past simple).

Last week our teacher introduced us to a team of educational researchers. They invited us to take part in a survey. They asked us about our pets and our favourite subjects. They even measured us. The researchers collect information about teenagers and publish it in the newspapers. People use it to make comparisons. They now know, for example, that 15-year-old boys today are 23cm taller than 15-year-old boys in the 1830s! That surprised all of us.

> *Last week we were introduced to a team of educational researchers. We*
>
> ....
>
> ....
>
> ....
>
> ....
>
> ....
>
> ....
>
> ....

6 Now write the conversation between Nathan and his dad.

Dad: How was school today?

Nathan: Oh, it was OK. (We / take part) *We took part* in a survey. To start with, (we / give) *we were given* about 50 questions to answer.

Dad: What sort of questions (you / ask)
[1].. ?

Nathan: Oh, about pets and things.

Dad: Film stars and pop stars, I suppose.

Nathan: No, (we / not ask) [2].........................
.... about film stars and pop stars, actually. It was mostly about school. And (we / measure)
[3].. .

Dad: Why (you / measure) [4].....................
.... ?

Nathan: Because (they / want) [5]....................
.... to compare our heights with the heights of people 170 years ago.

Dad: Oh. So (you / learn) [6].......................
.... anything?

Nathan: Yes, I did, actually. We're 23 centimetres taller.

Dad: Really? (I / amaze) [7].........................
.... !

Nathan: Mm, it was a very good day. The survey (take) [8]...................... all afternoon. (We / miss) [9]...................
.... Geography, so (our Geography homework / not collect) [10] ....
....

Dad: Nathan. You have done your Geography homework, haven't you?

Nathan: Oh, is that the time? I must go.

Communication

Stay cool

7 Rewrite the conversations correctly. Then match them with two of the pictures.

1

A: There's no hot water in my bathroom.
Hello. You could do something about it?

B: I sorry about that. I send someone up.

Picture ☐

Hello. There's ....

....

....

....

2

A: I afraid I have to complain about the new receptionist. Is quite rude and unhelpful.

B: I have a word with her.

Picture ☐

....

....

....

....

Move on / Go for it

8 In your notebook, write conversations for the remaining two pictures in Exercise 7.

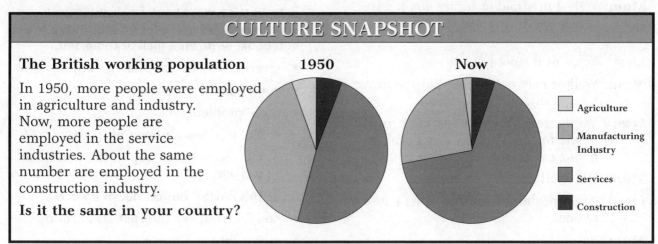

CULTURE SNAPSHOT

The British working population

In 1950, more people were employed in agriculture and industry. Now, more people are employed in the service industries. About the same number are employed in the construction industry.

Is it the same in your country?

1950   Now

Agriculture

Manufacturing Industry

Services

Construction

Boost your Writing 5

Dialogue

1 Complete the dialogue with the phrases in the box.

> * all right.   * ~~can you do me a favour?~~
> * Is that clear?   * It depends.   * It's a deal!
> * It's not my fault!   * Sorry to
> * there's nothing I can do about it.

Lisa: Mum, *can you do me a favour?*................
Can you sew this button on for me?

Mum: In a minute, Lisa. I've just had the phone bill and ...

Lisa: ¹.............................. interrupt, Mum, but I've got to go.

Mum: No, wait a minute. The bill is for £300. That's a lot! Most of the calls are to your friends.

Lisa: ².................................

Mum: Well, whose fault is it?

Lisa: I have to phone my friends.

Mum: But what do you talk about?

Lisa: ³............................ It's usually homework and the weekend.

Mum: Well, I'm afraid in future you'll have to ask before you use the phone.
⁴.............................

Lisa: Yes. But it's not fair.

Mum: Well, it may not be fair, but I'm afraid ⁵.............................

Lisa: Yes, there is. You can buy me a mobile phone for my birthday and I can buy phone cards with my pocket money.

Mum: Oh. Well, ⁶........................... .

Lisa: And I promise I won't use the house phone.

Mum: ⁷..............................

Text: An e-mail of complaint

2 Read the e-mail and number the sections in the correct order.

> | New ▾ | 🖅 Reply 🖅 Reply All 🖅 Forward | 🏳 Flag | 🖨 Print 🗑 Delete |
>
> **Outbox**
>
> ☐ I've had it for three weeks, and it has never worked properly. To start with, the ringing tone is too loud and I can't turn it down. Secondly, I often can't get the messages which my friends leave. Finally, it sometimes rings for no reason, which is really annoying.
>
> ☐ Yours faithfully,
>
> [1] Dear Sir / Madam
>
> ☐ Lisa Carling
>
> ☐ It was bought by my mother from your Internet Phone Shop. If I send it back to you, will you send me another one?
>
> ☐ I was recently given a Quantel 123 mobile phone for my birthday and I am really disappointed.
>
> ☐ I look forward to hearing from you as soon as possible.

Lisa makes three complaints about her phone. What are the words/phrases which she uses to introduce each one?

1 *To start with*..............................

2 ....

3 ....

3 Read the notes about a portable CD player which you were given for your birthday. In your notebook, write an e-mail of complaint.

* given to you by parents / grandparents ...
* you've had it for a month
* three problems:
  1 the top doesn't open properly
  2 CDs sometimes stop in the middle of a track
  3 the PAUSE button doesn't work
* bought from the Internet Hi-Fi shop
* give a refund / repair

13 If I had the money, ...

Grammar

Stay cool

Pronouns with *some-*, *any-*, *no-*, *every-*

1 Complete the sentences using a pronoun with *some-*, *any-*, *no-* or *every-*.

It's a secret. It's ..*nothing*.. to do with you.

1 Why do you criticise .... I do?

2 I'm afraid there's .... you can do.

3 I've got .... to tell you.

4 Does .... fancy a pizza?

5 There isn't .... to get a drink near here.

6 I'm going shopping. I've got .... to wear to Jake's party.

Second conditional: *if* clause + *'d (would)/wouldn't*

2 Use the verbs in brackets to make second conditional sentences.

If (I / can) *I could* do one thing to improve life in my city, (I / not allow) *I wouldn't allow* traffic to come into the centre. And (I / give) *I'd give* everyone a bike.

1 If (he / not be) .... so shy, (he / go out) .... more. (He / not stay) .... at home so much.

2 **A:** If (you / have) .... the choice, (you / go) .... and live in Australia?

   B: Yes, but (I / not want) .... to leave all my friends. (I / take) .... them with me!

Move on

Pronouns with *some-*, *any-*, *no-*, *every-*

3 Complete the conversations using a pronoun with *some-*, *any-*, *no-* or *every-*.

A: There's ..*someone*.. at the door.

B: OK. I'll go.

A: That's strange. There was [1]...................... there.

A: I can't find my keys [2]........................... . I've looked [3]........................... for them. Maybe [4]...........................'s taken them by mistake.

B: No, I'm sure [5]...............................'s taken them. They'll be here [6]........................... .

A: What's the matter?

B: There's [7]........................ to do. There isn't [8]........................ on TV, and [9].................... has gone away for the weekend, so there's [10]........................... to go.

A: Oh, cheer up. Perhaps there's [11]........................... on at the Blues Café.

B: The Blues Café? Forget it. [12]........................... goes there any more.

Second conditional: *if* clause + *'d (would)/wouldn't*

4 Use the verbs in the box in the correct tense to complete the sentences.

- be   • explain   • ~~go~~   • have   • can
- save   • talk   • take   • understand
- want   • ~~not feel~~   • make   • not refuse
- not stay up

If you ..*went*.. to bed early, you ..*wouldn't feel*.. tired all the time.

1 If we .... the bus rather than the train, we .... money.

2 If I .... in trouble, I know I .... talk to you.

3 If they .... so late, they .... more energy.

4 If she .... to more people, she .... friends.

5 If you .... the problem to your parents, I'm sure they ....

6 If he .... to borrow my camera, I ....

Go for it

Pronouns with *some-, any-, no-, every-*

5 In your notebook, write about your ideal holiday using at least four of the following pronouns.

- something • somewhere • somebody
- anything • anywhere • anybody
- nothing • nowhere • nobody
- everything • everywhere • everybody

Say:

- where you would or wouldn't go.
- what sort of person you would or wouldn't go with.
- what sort of things you would or wouldn't take.
- what sort of things you would or wouldn't do.

My ideal holiday

I would go to an island somewhere in the South Pacific.

I wouldn't go anywhere that was full of tourists ...

Second conditional: *if* clause + *'d (would)/wouldn't*

6 Write second conditional sentences to show what Jay is thinking.

Only if he finds out.

Oh, no! I'm not free on Tuesday evening.

Perhaps we can borrow a tent and go camping.

Maybe I should tidy my room.

Don't chat so much.

Friend:	We need someone to play in goal in Tuesday evening's match.	
Jay:	If *I were free on Tuesday evening, I'd play.*	
1 **Mum:**	I'm fed up with tidying your room, Jay. I'm going to stop your pocket money.	
Jay:	If	
2 **Brother:**	I'm in trouble for being late for school. Dad's going to be angry.	
Jay:	If	
3 **Friend:**	Why don't we go away somewhere this weekend?	
Jay:	If	
4 **Sister:**	My mobile phone bill's really expensive this month!	
Jay:	If	

Vocabulary

Stay cool

7 Match the pictures with the words.

a)

b)

c)

d)

e)

f)

g)

1	loud	_c)_	5	kind	....
2	sociable	......	6	generous	....
3	bossy	......	7	quick-tempered	....
4	quiet	......			

Move on

8 Complete the words.

A good friend is someone who is ...

d e p <u>e n d a</u> b l e

1 k _ _ d
2 l _ _ _ l
3 r _ _ _ a b l e
4 s y _ _ _ _ _ _ t i c

Go for it

9 Complete the responses.

A: You look a bit tired. And you've got a few spots, haven't you?

B: You're so _critical_ !

1 **A:** I never lend money and I never give money to charity.

B: You're so .... !

2 **A:** I just start crying if someone criticises my work.

B: You're too ....

3 **A:** I don't mind if you're late. You can arrive when you like.

B: You're very ....

4 **A:** Stop laughing. This is not a joke.

B: You're so .... !

Stay cool

10 Put the dialogue in the correct order.

1 **g** 2☐ 3☐ 4☐ 5☐ 6☐ 7☐ 8☐

a) I can't do that!

b) I think I'm in love.

c) If I were you, I'd send her a note and tell her.

d) Krisha. I really like her, but I'm shy. What do you think I should do?

e) Volleyball? That's a much better idea. OK.

f) Well, if you don't want to do that, why don't you ask her if she wants to play volleyball after school?

g) What's the matter with you?

h) Oh, no, not again! Who with?

Move on

11 Write Justin's part of the conversation using the phrases in the box.

- pretend to be ill
- just go for a short time
- ~~refuse~~
- suggest that she goes on her own

Craig: Alice wants to go to Anna's party this evening, but I don't. What should I do?

Justin: *If I were you, I'd refuse.*

Craig: I can't do that. Anna's her best friend.

Justin: ¹ ....
....

Craig: I'm not sure about that. She knows I'm not ill.

Justin: ² ....
....

Craig: I suppose I could. But she wants me to go with her.

Justin: ³ ....
....

Craig: That's true. If we were only there for an hour, it'd be OK.

Go for it

12 Write the conversation.

A: (*asks for advice*) Robin and Jack have invited me to go on holiday with them next year, but I haven't got enough money. What .... ?

B: (*gives advice:* parents)
....
....

A: (*rejects the advice*)
....
....

B: (*gives advice:* part-time job)
....
....

A: (*accepts the advice*)
....
....

STUDY CORNER

Rules with *some* and *any*

1 Is anything wrong?   3 Is anyone there?
2 Is something wrong?   4 Is someone there?

Although we usually use *any-* with questions, you can use *some-* if you think the answer is going to be 'yes'.

The person who asks question 2 thinks there **is** something wrong.

The person who asks question 4 thinks there **is** someone there.

Is it the same in your language?

14 Someone had dropped it.

Vocabulary

Stay cool

1 They're pop icons, but who are they? Complete the words for types of music to find out.

rhythm 'n' [ ] [ ] [ ] [E] [S]
[ ] [ ] [C] [K] 'n' roll
[T] [ ] [ ] [O] music
hip [H] [ ] [ ]

heavy [ ] [ ] [A] [L]
[C] [L] [ ] [ ] [A] [L] music
[ ] [N] [C] [E] music
[F] [L] music
[C] [ ] [R] [Y] and ...
[W] [ ] [ ] [T]
[G] [R] [G] [E] music

Move on

2 Answer the questions.

1 What do you call someone who ...

   composes music?   *a composer*

  a) plays the drums?   ....

  b) sings?   ....

  c) conducts an orchestra?   ....

2 What instrument does ... play?

   a cellist   *the cello*

  a) a guitarist   ....

  b) a pianist   ....

  c) a violinist   ....

Go for it

3 Which types of music do you associate with the following?

the 1930s, Louis Armstrong and Ella Fitzgerald   *jazz*..........

1 the 1950s, *Rock around the Clock* and Elvis Presley   ....

2 the 1960s Aretha Franklin and Stevie Wonder   ....

3 the 1970s, Bob Marley, Jamaica and the UK   ....

4 the 1980s, The Clash, short spiky hair and nose rings   ....

5 the 1990s, MC Hammer, fast, rhythmical talking with an instrumental background   ....

Stay cool

Past perfect simple

4 Use the prompts to make sentences about the characters.

It was Matt's first time in Cornwall. (He not be / there before)

He hadn't been there before.

1 Nicola started work in reception. (she work / in a hotel before?)

....

....

2 Nicola was a bit tired. (She not sleep / very well)

....

3 Matt talked about the waves in Hawaii. (Tom / never / go / to Hawaii)

....

....

4 Nicola went to the surf shop. Matt wasn't there. (He / already / leave)

....

5 Tom was working really hard. (He / not have / a day off since Friday)

....

....

6 Morris was angry with Nicola. (She / be / impolite / to a guest)

....

....

7 Tom was a bit quiet. (Matt / just / walk in)

....

too many, too much, (not) enough

5 Complete the conversation with the correct form of *there was/were* and *too much, too many, (not) enough*.

Mark: You seem a bit fed up. Didn't you enjoy the party?

Ruby: It was OK, but it was very crowded. *There were too many* people there. We had to stand all the time because [1]................................. chairs to sit on.

Mark: Yes, I suppose so. But the music was good.

Ruby: Mm. If you like that sort of thing. [2]................................. boring old reggae stuff and [3].............................. good R'n'B, if you ask me. Anyway, it was impossible to dance because [4]................................. space.

Mark: And the food was good. Your chocolate cake was a great success.

Ruby: [5].................................... for everybody? I hope so.

Mark: What did you think of the olive bread which Kate made?

Ruby: It was OK if you like bread with bits in. For me, [6]..................................... .... olives in it.

Mark: Oh, well, I enjoyed it.

Reported requests and commands

6 Report what Mark said to Ruby after the party.

tell

1 Cheer up.

Don't get depressed.

He *told her to cheer up.* ....

He ....

ask

2 Could you make me a cake?

....

Please don't put any nuts in it.

....

want

3 Come round for a barbecue.

....

You don't need to bring anything.

....

Move on

Past perfect simple
Reported requests and commands

7 Complete the sentences.

We arrived late at Mum's office and
she'd already gone home. ....

The security guard *told us to phone her.* ....

They couldn't get into the restaurant

because Guy [1] ....

Lisa didn't want [2] ....

Jo knew where Gina and David were

because [3] ....

They asked her [4] ....

I couldn't go out last night because [5] ....

....

Dad told me [6] ....

I was locked out. [7] ....

....

My friend asked me [8] ....

They were hungry because [9] ....

....

Jack's mum told them [10] ....

....

Go for it

Reported requests and commands

8 You've just finished your first day as a waiter/waitress in a restaurant. Here are some of the things the head waiter said to you. Tell your friend about them, using the verbs *tell*, *ask* and *want*.

> Do not run into the kitchen.

1 Please wear a white shirt next time.
2 Be polite to the customers at all times.
3 Put all tips into the box on the desk.
4 Please don't chat to the customers.
5 Remember that the customer is always right.

He told me not to run into the kitchen.
....

1 ....
....
2 ....
....
3 ....
....
4 ....
....
5 ....
....

Write three more things the head waiter said to you about:

• smiling;

• checking the orders;

• talking to the other waiters all the time.

Then change them into reported requests/commands.

....
....
....
....
....
....
....
....
....
....
....
....

Communication

Stay cool

9 It's the evening before you leave for your holidays. Your friend's mother has taken you and your friend to the cinema. Complete the conversation.

You: Thank you for a very ..*nice*.. evening.

Friend's mum: I'm [1]......... you could come.

You: So [2].......... I. It was a good film.

Friend's mum: Yes, it was, [3].................... it? I enjoyed it [4].......... .

You: And thanks [5].......... the guidebook.

Friend's mum: [6]...................... welcome. I hope it's useful.

You: I'm [7].................... it will be.

Friend's mum: Well, have a good trip.

You: Thanks.

Move on / Go for it

10 Your friend invited you to stay for the weekend. It is Sunday evening, and you are about to leave. In your notebook, write the conversation using the ideas below.

• You enjoyed the weekend a lot.

• You really liked playing volleyball on the beach.

• Your friend enjoyed the barbecue on the beach in the evening.

• Your friend suggests going walking in the mountains next month.

You: *Thanks. That was a great weekend.*

Friend: *I'm glad ...*

Boost your Writing 6

Text: Write a review of an event

1 Read the review of a concert at the Eden Project. Match the topic headings to the correct paragraphs.

a) People's opinion of the event ☐

b) The location, time and weather ☐ `1`

c) The performers ☐

d) The audience ☐

1 The Eden Project, ...*where*... people normally spend the day exploring the huge bio-domes, was the setting for a wonderful concert last night. The concert took place outside the domes, ¹............... were lit up for the occasion. It was a fine, dry night and the atmosphere was electric.

2 Beth Orton and Doves, ².................. were first on stage, were fantastic. But the stars of the evening were Jarvis Cocker and his band, Pulp. They played songs from their album *We Love Life*, ³............... features lyrics about the Earth and nature.

3 Three thousand people attended the event, ⁴................. was organised by the Eden Project to raise money for musicians in other countries. There were many people from Cornwall, ⁵.............. the Eden Project is situated, as well as Pulp fans from all over the country in the audience.

4 At the end of the concert, a member of the audience ⁶............ was sitting next to me said, 'That was a truly magical evening.' And I had to agree.

2 Add the relative pronouns *who*, *which* and *where* to complete the text.

3 You can make your writing more interesting by varying the length of your sentences. In your notebook, join these sentences using *who*, *which* or *where*. Note that some sentences can be joined in more than one way.

The concert took place last Sunday. It was attended by 100,000 people.

The concert, which was attended by 100,000 people, took place last Sunday.

The concert, which took place last Sunday, was attended by 100,000 people.

1 The lead singer is also a fantastic guitarist. He comes from Ireland.

2 The tickets were sold in two hours. They were £25 each.

3 It was in Hyde Park. The Jubilee Rock Concert took place there.

4 The best part was meeting Ms Dynamite. She gave me her autograph.

5 The concert raised half a million pounds. It was also shown on TV.

6 I had the chance to go backstage. I saw bands getting ready to perform.

4 In your notebook, write a review of an event. It can be one you went to or one you saw on TV. Use the same sequence of topics as in the Eden Project concert review. Try to use *who*, *which* and *where*.

The Wheels of Fortune

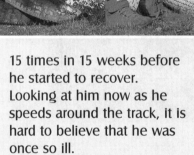

I want to be the Formula One World Champion

– Luke Hines

The flag is lowered and they're off! They speed around the circuit at 100 kilometres an hour. This is the serious motor sport of Karting, one of the most exciting sports there is, and one which young people can take part in. It's also good training for people who want to become Formula One racing drivers. Not surprisingly, many Formula One drivers, including David Coulthard and Michael Schumacher, learned how to drive fast in Karts.

Luke Hines, 14, is the Vice European Karting champion. He is very determined to be successful. At the age of six, he had a serious accident when a tractor ran over his leg. Doctors had to operate 15 times in 15 weeks before he started to recover. Looking at him now as he speeds around the track, it is hard to believe that he was once so ill.

Two years after the accident, Luke first drove a Kart. Then, at the age of ten, he was selected to join the Young Guns team, which gives young drivers the opportunity to race.

'Joining the Young Guns was the turning point for me,' said Luke. 'I began to train more and more and, before long, I was winning competitions.'

One of Luke's best friends and biggest rivals is Gary Paffett, 15, who was the winner of the McClaren Mercedes Champions of the Future series for drivers between the ages of nine and 16. Gary, too, was selected to join the Young Guns team.

What about the future? The boys aim to link up with a clothing sponsor and become racing models. If they managed to do a deal with a clothing company, it would help them to buy designer clothes, which they love.

'I want to be the Formula One World Champion,' says Luke. But motor racing is an expensive sport, so you need sponsorship. If he gets the right sponsors, he'll have a very good chance of achieving his dream. And he'll have great clothes to wear, too!

Comprehension

Stay cool

1 Find words or phrases that mean the same as:

to go fast	*to speed*
1 a farm vehicle with large back wheels	....
2 to get better	....
3 chosen	....
4 the chance	....
5 the moment when things change	....
6 competitors	....
7 to reach an agreement	....
8 someone who gives money or equipment	....

Move on

2 Answer these questions.

What happens at the beginning of a race?

The flag is lowered.

1 How fast do the drivers go?

....

2 Luke had an accident when he was young. What happened?

....

3 How old was Luke when he started Karting?

....

4 Why is the Young Guns team special?

....

5 Why do racing drivers need sponsors?

....

Go for it

3 Find ...

1 two good things about Karting. *It's exciting.*

....

2 three things which Luke and Gary have in common.

....

....

Communication

4 Luke gave you free tickets to watch a race he was in. Complete the conversation.

Luke: Did you enjoy the race?

You: (*thank him; express pleasure*)

¹ *Yes, I did, thanks.*

....

Luke: I was offered a sponsorship deal with a clothing company yesterday. What do you think I should do?

You: (*say what you would do – accept it!*)

² ....

Luke: Hm. I don't know.

You: (*show surprise that he isn't excited about it*)

³ ....

Luke: Well, I may be able to get a better deal from another company.

You: (*give your own advice*)

⁴ ....

....

Luke: Yes, you may be right.

Writing

5 In your notebook, write a paragraph for a magazine about Ben Skinner.

Name	Ben Skinner
Age	17
Sport	Surfing – started when he was very young
Countries visited	Brazil, South Africa, Australia
Sponsors	Three beach clothing companies help him with air fares
Competitions	2001 Winner, English Longboard competition 2001 2ⁿᵈ, British Schools Competition

Ben Skinner, 17, is an international surfer. He ...

Vocabulary

Stay cool

1 Complete the sentences with the correct form of the words in the box. Use each word twice.

• build • cook • heat • hunt • sing

If you have to catch your dinner, you have to be a good _hunter_ !

1 Big, old houses are often very cold. .... them is a problem.

2 Do you think fox .... should be banned?

3 Our flat is in a .... which dates from the 1920s.

4 That pasta dish was delicious. You're a good ....

5 The garden wall has fallen down. We need to call the ....

6 She's got a good voice, but she doesn't like .... in public.

7 There's an electric .... if it gets cold in here.

8 You spend a lot of time in the kitchen. Do you like .... ?

9 You won't be a good .... unless you learn to breathe properly.

Move on

2 What occupation does each group of words suggest? All the words end in *-er* or *-or*.

travelling to a place and deciding to live there — _settler_

1 paints, paper, landscapes — ....

2 animals, crops, land — ....

3 travelling to remote places and finding out about them — ....

4 designing and making sculptures — ....

5 school, helping pupils to learn — ....

6 writing music — ....

Go for it

3 For each prompt, write a sentence using a noun ending in *-er* or *-or*.

He's the head of the marketing department, but he's no good at dealing with people.

He isn't a good manager.

1 The way she moves in time to the music is fantastic.

....

....

2 I'm never going in the car with him again.

....

....

3 I think her books are amazing. I read them as soon as they come out.

....

....

4 When he's in a play, you feel he really becomes the character.

....

....

5 He's a good musician, but he always feels ill before he plays to an audience.

....

....

Stay cool

Verb *used to*

4 Write what Harriet is thinking using *used to/didn't use to* with the verbs in the box.

> • climb • eat • fight • go • ~~have~~ • have • wear

I used to have a cat called Fluffy.

4 .... long hair.

1 .... to nursery school.

5 .... glasses.

2 .... carrots.

3 .... trees.

6 .... with my sister.

so and *such a/an* + adjective + noun

5 What are Nicola and Tom thinking? Complete the sentences.

Matt is _such a_ pain at times!
1 Tom is .... kind and sensible.
2 I had .... awful day yesterday!
3 Some of the hotel guests are .... rude.
4 Morris can be .... bossy at times.
5 I was in .... bad mood after work.

6 Is Matt .... brilliant surfer?
7 He thinks he's .... cool!
8 He's .... sociable person.
9 Nicola was .... helpful when she was teaching me to bowl.
10 It was .... great concert!
11 I was .... pleased that Matt wasn't there.

16

Move on / Go for it

Verb *used to*

6 Look at the photo and read the information. Then write questions and answers using *used to*.

1891	Schools stopped charging for education. Lessons included reading, writing and arithmetic.
1906	School meals were introduced at some schools. Pupils over the age of nine could work and go to school.
1918	Children under the age of twelve were not allowed to work.

What did schoolgirls use to wear?

They used to wear aprons over their ordinary clothes.

1 Why was 1891 an important year?

Because before 1891, schools ....

....

....

2 ....

....

They used to sit at wooden desks.

3 What about school subjects?

....

....

4 What about meals at school?

Before 1906, pupils ....

....

....

5 ....

.... ?

Yes. Before 1918, some pupils used to go to school and work.

so and *such* with a clause of result

7 Match the sentences and join them using *so* or *such* and a clause of result.

1 She's been very busy.
2 I was really thirsty.
3 He was very tired.
4 It was a very boring film.
5 They had a really good holiday.
6 I'm very hungry.

a) I could eat two pizzas.
b) He went to bed as soon as he got home.
c) We left after ten minutes.
d) She hasn't had time for lunch.
e) They're planning to go again next year.
f) I drank a litre of water.

1 [d] *She's been so busy that she hasn't had time for lunch.*

2 ☐ ....

3 ☐ ....

4 ☐ ....

5 ☐ ....

6 ☐ ....

Stay cool

8 You're in London with your family. You want to take a boat trip. Complete the conversation using details of your own family.

You: (*Ask for your tickets.*)

1 ....

tickets to Tower Bridge and back, please?

Assistant: Certainly.

You: (*Ask the price.*)

2 .... ?

Assistant: £8.00 for adults and £4.00 for children under 14.

You: (*Ask about special rates for students.*)

3 .... ?

Assistant: Yes. For students, it's £5.00.

You: (*Say how many tickets you want for adults, students and children.*)

4 ....

Assistant: Can I see your student card(s), please?

You: (*You haven't got it/them with you.*)

5 ....

....

Assistant: I'm sorry, but you have to have a student card to get a reduction.

You: Oh, OK.

Assistant: Here you are. That's 6 ....
altogether, please.

CULTURE SNAPSHOT

The Thames

There are several bridges over the River Thames. The most famous is Tower Bridge, which opens to let tall ships pass through. The most recent bridge, the Millennium Bridge, was built to celebrate the year 2000. People now walk by the river more than they used to because there are new paths along its banks.

**Does a river run through your city?
Can you walk by it for a long way?**

Move on / Go for it

9 You and a group of friends want to go to a photography exhibition. Read the information and write the dialogue in your notebook.

The Hayward Gallery

Photography Exhibition

Ansel Adams – Images of the American West
Tickets £8

Hayward Shop
Books, posters, postcards and gifts

School groups £2 per person

Hayward Café
The café serves a range of drinks and food.

You: (Greet the assistant and ask about the price of tickets.)

Assistant: (Give the price of a single ticket.)

You: (Express surprise. Ask about school groups.)

Assistant: (Respond. Ask for student cards.)

You: (Respond. Ask about what you can buy.)

Assistant: (Respond.)

You: (Ask about somewhere for lunch.)

Assistant: (Respond)

You: (Thank the assistant.)

What's wrong?

10 Circle and correct the mistakes.

You're a very good (cooker).

You're a very good cook.

1 It's a such good song.

....

2 I enjoyed the film so much so I want to see it again.

....

3 We use to see each other every day.

....

4 It's such a terrible weather today.

....

5 £5 and £7, that's £12 together.

....

17 He said he'd been away.

Grammar

Stay cool

Reported statements

1 Change the statements into reported speech.

'I usually go into town on Saturdays.'

She said *she usually went into town on Saturdays.*

1 'I enjoy ice-skating.'

She said ....

2 'I'm trying to get to sleep.'

He said ....

3 'I wrote to Karl.'

He said ....

4 'We haven't seen Darren.'

They said ....

5 'I'll phone Claire.'

She said ....

6 'We can't come to the party.'

They said ....

2 Report what these students said about their plans.

I didn't do very well in my Maths exam. I want to improve.

Michael said he hadn't done very well in his Maths exam. He said he wanted to improve.

1 I need to save money. I'll get a Saturday job.

Ben said ....

....

....

....

....

2 I haven't kept in touch with my penfriend. I'm going to write once a week.

Camilla said ....

....

....

....

....

3 My mum has a lot to do. I can help more in the house.

Simon said ....

....

....

....

4 My brother is always positive and helpful. I'm going to try to be more like him.

Leesun said ....

....

....

....

....

5 I talk too much, but I can't help it!

Suzanne said ....

....

....

....

....

Move on

Reported statements

3 You've just received an e-mail from Amy, who's travelling in Scotland with Joel. You're telling a friend about it:

'She said they'd spent three wonderful days in Edinburgh. They'd arrived on Tuesday. She said Joel was particularly keen on the shops. They'd never be able to carry all the stuff he'd bought. She was e-mailing from an Internet café. She could see the castle from where she was sitting. She hoped we weren't jealous!'

Write the e-mail which Amy wrote.

🖉 New ▾	🖅 Reply 🖅 Reply All 🖅 Forward	🏳 Flag	🖨 Print 🗑 Delete	🖂 Send & Receive ▾	📖 Address Book 🔍 Find

Outbox   subject ◆ starts with ◆

| 🖅 ❄ ! 🖉 | To | Subject | Sent |

Joel and I have spent three wonderful days in Edinburgh. We ....

....

....

....

....

....

Amy

Go for it

4 You interviewed these people about their impressions of Scotland. Write an article about them in your notebook. Use *say*, *tell* or *think* to introduce what they said.

The first person I spoke to was Mateo, from Spain. He said he didn't like the weather.

Then I spoke to Eleonora, from Italy. She thought Scotland …

'We're hoping to find part-time jobs here. We haven't made up our minds how long we'll stay. But it won't be more than six weeks, unfortunately.'
Sarah and Chloe, *England*

'I don't like the weather!'
Mateo, *Spain*

'People seem very relaxed. I'm having such a good time that I'll have to come back!'
Joana, *Romania*

'It's great! You can eat really well. Even the pizzas are good!'
Eleonora, *Italy*

'I didn't expect people to be so friendly.'
Adam, *Poland*

Stay cool

5 In each conversation, use one of the words in the first person's sentence to make a new word to complete what the second person says.

A: She performed that solo really well.

B: I know, she's a brilliant _performer_ .

1 **A:** Are you related to Rose?

 B: Yes, but she's not a close ....

2 **A:** She's a psychologist.

 B: Oh, yes. She studied .... at university, didn't she?

3 **A:** You seem to think that exams aren't important.

 B: No, you're wrong. I understand the .... of exams.

4 **A:** We're living through a technological revolution.

 B: Yes. Information .... has changed our lives.

5 **A:** I was astonished that he won the competition.

 B: Well, my .... was greater than yours!

Move on

6 Make nouns from these verbs, using *-ion*, *-ment* or *-ance*.

Where's the entr_ance_ ....?

1 What's the big attract.................. ?

2 When is their next appear.................. ?

3 We had a disagree.................. .

4 Do you want to see my coin collect.................. ?

5 What's all this excite.................. about?

6 You can't live in ignor.................. .

7 There's been a big improve................ in your grades.

8 There's a Roman settle................ on top of the hill.

9 The sun is very strong, so you'll need protect................ .

10 I sometimes read books in translat................. .

Go for it

7 Solve the puzzle to find the mystery word.

1 Work that you do to earn money.
2 A machine which processes information.
3 A musician or an actor gives this.
4 A person who creates a set of instructions for Number 2.
5 You get this at school and college.
6 You go to the Tourist Office for this.
7 The science of living things.
8 Something which has a big effect is of great ... .
9 Another word for 'amazement'.
10 Someone who has a connection to your family.
11 The people who decide what happens in a country.
12 The number of kilometres between one place and another.

The mystery word is: ....

Communication

Stay cool

8 Rewrite the dialogue in the correct order.

Alex	Tanya
• I don't know. He didn't say. Can I take a message?	• Oh, I see. Can I speak to Sanjay, please?
• I'm afraid he's out.	• Hello. Who am I speaking to?
• OK. I'll tell him you called.	• Thanks. Bye.
• (Hello.)	• When will he be back?
• It's Alex. I'm a friend of Sanjay's.	• No, thanks, it doesn't matter. I'll ring back later.

Alex: *Hello.* ....

Tanya: [1] ....

....

Alex: [2] ....

....

Tanya: [3] ....

....

Alex: [4] ....

Tanya: [5] ....

Alex: [6] ....

....

Tanya: [7] ....

....

Alex: [8] ....

Tanya: [9] ....

Move on / Go for it

9 In your notebook, write the conversation for the following situation.

• You phone the sports centre to speak to the manager.

• The receptionist isn't sure that she's in her office. She checks. She isn't in, so the receptionist offers to take a message.

• You'd rather phone back later.

• You phone later and speak to the receptionist. This time the manager is in.

Receptionist: Leewood Sports Centre. Can I help you?

You: ...

What's wrong?

10 Circle and correct the mistakes.

Hello. (Is) Laurie speaking. Can I help you?

Hello. Laurie speaking. Can I help you? ....

1 It's OK. I ring back later.

....

2 He told that he loved her.

....

3 She said she like chocolate ice cream.

....

....

4 So you're playing hard to get are you?

....

....

STUDY CORNER

Verbs and nouns

When you look up a verb in your dictionary, find out whether a noun can be formed from it. Note any spelling changes.

> **de·scribe** /dɪˈskraɪb/ *verb* (*present participle* describing, *past* described) to say what someone or something is like

> **de·scrip·tion** /dɪˈskrɪpʃn/ *noun* an account of what someone or something is like

11 Using your dictionary, write the nouns which come from the following verbs. They end in *-ment*, *-ion*, *-er* or *-or*.

emigrate *emigration* ....

employ *employment, employer*

1 manage ....

2 construct ....

3 invent ....

4 introduce ....

5 create ....

6 communicate ....

7 direct ....

Boost your Writing 7

Dialogue

1 Complete the dialogue with the phrases in the box.

- she was annoyed with you
- I haven't had time.
- you hadn't kept in touch
- I haven't made up my mind
- ~~she was missing me~~
- You're playing hard to get,
- I couldn't get through.

Nick and his sister Daisy are on holiday in Dublin with their parents.

Daisy: That was Martha on the phone.

Nick: Oh, really? Did she say _she was missing me?_

Daisy: No chance! She said [1]....................... .... because [2].. ....

Nick: Oh.

Daisy: You told her you'd send her an e-mail, and you haven't even done that.

Nick: [3]... .

Daisy: Why didn't you phone her?

Nick: I tried, but [4]..................................... ....

Daisy: Oh, yeah? I bet! Anyway, you could send her a text message.

Nick: It's not the same.

Daisy: She said she was going to Daniel's party. Are you going to go?

Nick: I don't know. [5]................................ .... yet.

Daisy: [6]... , ... aren't you?

Nick: No!

Daisy: Be careful. You might succeed.

Text: Write an article about a place

2 Read the text and write the following time words in the correct places:

- in   - from   - for   - since   - to

Ireland

DUBLIN

Trinity College

Trinity College was founded __in__ 1592 by Queen Elizabeth I, and it has been Ireland's most famous university [1].......... that date. The main reason for visiting Trinity College is to see one of the oldest books in the world. This is the *Book of Kells*, which was written [2].......... the ninth century. It has been in the library of Trinity College [3].......... nearly fifty years. You can also visit 'The Dublin Experience', a multimedia presentation which tells the story of Dublin and its people [4].......... early times [5].......... the present day.

Temple Bar

Temple Bar is an area near the River Liffey. It has lots of interesting restaurants and clubs. You'll also find the oldest shop in Dublin in the Temple Bar area. It's been there [6].......... 240 years. But if you're looking for something a bit more modern, don't worry. You'll also find plenty of shops which have opened [7]......... then.

Phoenix Park

Phoenix Park is twice as big as New York's Central Park. Dublin Zoo is one of the main attractions [8].......... the park. The zoo was opened [9]......... 1830. Áras an Uachtaráin, the home of the Irish President, is also in the Phoenix Park. It was built [10].......... 1751.

3 In your notebook, write an article for a guidebook about a town or city. Use the article about Dublin as a model.

First, make notes under the following headings.

- **A famous building**
  Date   History   Main reason for going
  Other attractions

- **A popular area of the city**
  Location   Attractions

- **A popular open space** (e.g. a park)
  Size   History   Attractions

Then write the article. Try to include the time expressions *in*, *from*, *for*, *since* and *to*.

18 Jamaica Inn

Vocabulary

Stay cool

1 Number the time expressions in order from the most recent to the furthest away in time.

a) a couple of days ago ☐

b) a few days ago ☐

c) a couple of minutes ago ☐ 1

d) several hours ago ☐

e) about a quarter of an hour ago ☐

2 Use phrases from the box to replace the phrases in italics. Use each phrase once only.

- hundreds of
- lots of
- loads of
- a couple of
- a few
- several

Our school did four performances of the musical 'West Side Story' *two weeks ago*. We'd practised the songs and the dance routines for ¹*about ten weeks* and then we had the dress rehearsal. We made ²*one or two mistakes*, but the drama teacher gave us ³*a huge amount of encouragement*, and we were fine on the first night. Over the four nights, ⁴*eight or nine hundred people* came to see us. ⁵*Many parents* came, of course. And there was a reporter from the local newspaper. Fame at last!

a couple of weeks ago ....

1 ....

2 ....

3 ....

4 ....

5 ....

Move on / Go for it

3 Complete the conversations. Include the following expressions of time and quantity.

- a couple of minutes • for ages
- lots of • for some time • ~~loads of~~
- about a quarter of an hour ago

> It's August 4th and Kate is having a birthday barbecue. She's just bought two hundred sausages.

Mum: Will there be enough food?

Kate: *Yes. I've bought loads of sausages.* ....

1
> They haven't used the barbecue since June.

Kate: Is the barbecue OK?

Mum: I don't know. ....

....

2
> It's 7 o'clock. Kate's father went out at about 6.45. Her mother wonders where he's gone.

Mum: Where's your father?

Kate: ....

....

3
> Kate's friend Tim wants a milkshake. Kate can make one in two minutes.

Tim: I'd love a milkshake.

Kate: ....

....

4
> Kate meets Jan, who she hasn't seen since she was ten years old.

Jan: Hello!

Kate: ....

....

5
> Tim comments on how many people are there. Kate is really pleased.

Tim: Great barbecue. ....

....

Kate: Thanks. I'm glad you're enjoying it.

Stay cool

Reported questions

4 Change these direct questions into reported questions.

Are you in St Ives on holiday?

He asked her *if she was in St Ives on holiday.*

....

What time did you arrive?

He asked her *what time she had arrived.*

....

1 Do you like St Ives?

He asked her ....

....

2 Can I come home with you?

He asked him ....

....

3 Is the surfing good?

He asked him ....

....

4 Have you seen my sunglasses?

She asked her ....

....

5 Where have you been?

He asked her ....

....

6 Have you worked in a restaurant before?

He asked her ....

....

7 What's happened?

She asked him ....

....

8 How much was the tea towel?

She asked her ....

....

9 Did you enjoy the disco the other night?

He asked her ....

....

10 Why hasn't he kept in touch?

She asked her ....

....

5 Can you remember who asked the questions and who they were talking to?

Matt asked Nicola. ....

Tom asked Nicola. ....

1 ....

2 ....

3 ....

4 ....

5 ....

6 ....

7 ....

8 ....

9 ....

10 ....

The answers are below.

Answers to Exercise 5
Matt asked Nicola: Unit 2   *Tom asked Nicola: Unit 1*
1 Matt asked Nicola: Unit 1   2 Jamie asked Tom: Unit 3   3 Tom asked Matt: Unit 4   4 Nicola asked Louise: Unit 6
5 Tom asked Nicola: Unit 6   6 Morris asked Nicola: Unit 7   7 Mrs Henley asked Tom: Unit 8   8 Nicola asked Mrs Henley: Unit 8
9 Matt asked Nicola: Unit 13   10 Nicola asked Louise: Unit 17

Move on / Go for it

Reported questions
Reported statements

6 Read the survey and answer the interviewer's questions. Then report your answers.

Teenage survey

Name: ....

Age: ....

Family and home

1 Who do you live with?
2 Do you have to help at home?

Education and skills

3 What do you like about school?
4 How much time do you spend on your homework?
5 How many subjects are you studying?
6 Are you studying anything outside school?

Leisure and travel

7 How do you spend your free time?
8 Have you ever been to another country?

Plans

9 What are your ambitions?
10 Where will you be in five years' time?

1 *She asked who I lived with. I told her ...* ....

2 ....
....

3 ....
....

4 ....
....

5 ....
....

6 ....
....

7 ....
....

8 ....
....

9 ....
....

10 ....
....

Stay cool

7 Circle the correct options.

May I *(put)*/ *to put* the TV on?

Yes, of course. Go *straight on* /*(ahead.)*

1 **A:** Is it all right *that* / *if* I use the phone?

   B: Yes, of course.

   A: I have to ring Sam. He asked me if I *did want* / *wanted* to go out this evening.

2 **A:** Do you mind *that* / *if* I open the window?

   B: *Yes,* / *No,* not at all.

Move on

8 Write the dialogues.

   A: (I / look at your magazine?)

   Do you mind if I look at your magazine?

   B: (✓)

   No, not at all.

   (✗ – not mine)

   Well, actually, it isn't mine.

   I'm afraid it isn't mine.

1 **A:** (I / sit here?)

   ....

   ....

   B: (✗ – seat is taken)

   ....

   ....

2 **A:** (we / have a look inside the theatre?)

   ....

   ....

   B: (✗ – closed)

   ....

   ....

3 **A:** (we / meet you outside the cinema?)

   ....

   ....

   B: (✓)

   ....

   ....

Go for it

9 Use the pictures and prompts to write a dialogue.

It's a cold winter's day. You're travelling by train to see some friends for the weekend. You've switched off your mobile phone because the battery is very low. You're reading. A woman gets into the compartment and sits opposite you.

Complete the conversation.

Woman: ¹ ....

You: ² ....

....

Woman: ³ ....

....

You: ⁴ ....

....

Woman: ⁵ ....

....

You: ⁶ ....

....

Woman: Well, goodbye. Have a nice journey!

You: ⁷ ....

19 He's too good to fall.

Grammar

Stay cool

too* + adjective + *to
Adjective + *enough*

1 Change these sentences into sentences using *too* or *enough*.

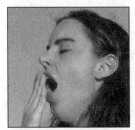

Rebecca: I'm tired.
I don't want to go out.

Rebecca was too tired to go out.

1 **Lily:** I'm really nervous.
I can't take my piano
exam.

....
....

2 **Mark:** I'm quite good at
football, but you have to
be very good to get into
the team.

....
....

3 **Sara:** I'm quite easy-
going. I don't think
I could be a teacher.

....
....

4 **Jack:** I'm fit, but I
couldn't swim 100
lengths.

....
....

5 **Lee:** My problem is
that I'm a bit shy.
I don't make friends
easily.

....
....

Verb + infinitive / gerund (*-ing* form)

2 Complete the sentences using the verbs in
brackets in the correct form.

I expect *to see* (see) Jamie and Charlotte
at the weekend.

1 Do you mind .... (look after)
my camera for a moment?

2 I wanted .... (go out) this evening.

3 You'll enjoy .... (go) to Spain.

4 Sara didn't seem .... (be)
frightened of anything.

5 Lauren has offered .... (take) us
home in her car.

6 Tom refused .... (answer).

7 The holiday was good, but I missed
.... (see) my friends.

8 Has Rob given up .... (smoke)?

Move on / Go for it

too + adjective + to
(not) + adjective + enough to

3 Nigel had a bad day yesterday. Look at the pictures and say what happened.
Use the adjectives with *too* or *enough* and match them with the phrases.

busy   compete in the race

fit   see the film

hot   see him

old   do his homework

tired   drink

Sorry, Nigel. I've got so much to do this evening ...

2 His girlfriend ....
....
....

His coffee
was too hot to drink.

3 He ....
....
....

1 He ....
....
....

4 He ....
....
....

4 Complete the e-mail from Anna to Maria.

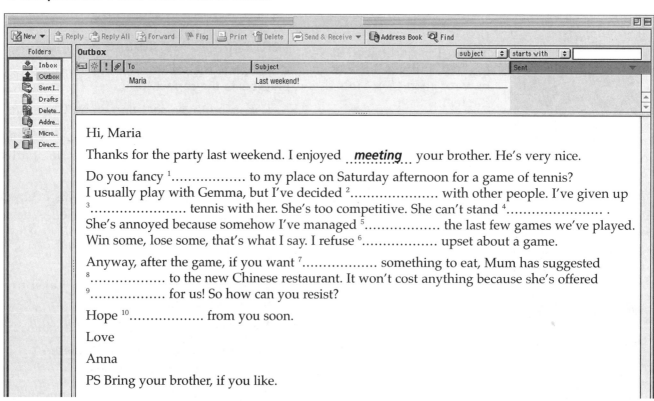

Hi, Maria

Thanks for the party last weekend. I enjoyed .....*meeting*..... your brother. He's very nice.

Do you fancy [1]................. to my place on Saturday afternoon for a game of tennis?
I usually play with Gemma, but I've decided [2].................... with other people. I've given up
[3].................... tennis with her. She's too competitive. She can't stand [4]...................... .
She's annoyed because somehow I've managed [5]................. the last few games we've played.
Win some, lose some, that's what I say. I refuse [6]................. upset about a game.

Anyway, after the game, if you want [7]................. something to eat, Mum has suggested
[8]................. to the new Chinese restaurant. It won't cost anything because she's offered
[9]................. for us! So how can you resist?

Hope [10]................. from you soon.

Love

Anna

PS Bring your brother, if you like.

Stay cool

5 Circle six more 'strong' adjectives in the wordsquare and match them with the neutral adjectives below.

R	I	J	D	B	K	F	T	N
S	E	N	O	R	M	O	U	S
T	E	R	R	I	F	I	E	D
A	X	G	R	L	R	A	D	M
R	H	U	T	L	S	B	K	O
V	A	G	C	I	F	E	A	L
I	U	Y	I	A	V	D	E	P
N	S	O	U	N	B	T	K	V
G	T	R	S	T	I	N	Y	A
T	E	R	R	I	B	L	E	T
L	D	W	Q	U	K	C	H	I

big	*enormous*
1 bad	....
2 hungry	....
3 small	....
4 tired	....
5 good	....
6 afraid	....

Move on

6 Complete each sentence with an adjective from the wordsquare in Exercise 5.

I was frightened. In fact, I was *terrified* .

1 I haven't eaten since yesterday.
I'm ....

2 My room at the hotel was ten metres long by ten metres wide. It was ....
....

3 The boy kept falling asleep.
He was ....

4 The weather was grey and wet the whole time.
It was ....

5 I always feel hungry when I've eaten at that restaurant. The portions are
....

Go for it

7 Complete the conversation using adjectives from Exercise 5.

Tim: That was a very .*good*. concert. Did you enjoy it?

Ann: I certainly did. It was ¹ .... !

Tim: Let's go and have something to eat. Are you ² .... ?

Ann: Yes, but I'm not ³ .... Maybe we could have some fish and chips or something.

Tim: You've had a very long day. You must be ⁴ ....

Ann: I'm a bit ⁵ .... , it's true.

Tim: OK, let's go to The Surf Hut.

Ann: Oh, no, not there. It's a ⁶ .... place. The chips are always cold and the portions are ⁷ .... !

Tim: What about a pizza?

Ann: Sounds good to me!

Stay cool

8 Circle the best response in each case.

Take care.   I hope so. / (I will.)

1 See you next year. Thanks. Same to you. /
                      I hope so.

2 Write to me.   I hope so. / OK. I will.

3 Don't work   I hope so. / Don't
   too hard!   worry, I won't!

4 Have a nice time.   I'm sure I will. /
                      I hope so.

5 I hope you get   Yes, so do I. / Yes, I
   good results in   will.
   your exams.

Move on

9 Write what people might say in these situations.

*Georgia is going on a Club 18–21 holiday.
She'll meet lots of people.*

Georgia: It's going to be great. Discos
              and beach parties every night!

Megan: Be good. Don't *do anything*
              I wouldn't do!

Lewis is going on holiday to Thailand.

Lewis: I won't see you for three
              months.

Sarah: [1].......................... a postcard.
              It would be good to hear from
              you.

Mrs Palmer is going to Seattle on business.

Mrs Palmer: OK, I'm off now. See you on
                 Friday.

Mr Palmer: [2].................................... trip.
                 I hope it's successful.

Mark is taking his driving test tomorrow.

Mark: It's my driving test tomorrow.

Justin: Good [3]................................. .
              Then you can take us all out in
              your new car!

*Julia is going on a study weekend to prepare for
her A-level exams.*

Julia: We start at 9.30 in the morning
              and don't finish till seven in the
              evening!

Mum: Well, [4].................................... .
              You don't want to get exhausted
              before the exams.

Go for it

10 Complete your part of the conversation.

*You've just spent a couple of weeks staying with
some family friends in the UK. You've had a
really good time.*

You: The taxi's here – time to go!

Friend: Unfortunately!

You: [1].............................. time.

Mother: It's been a pleasure.

You: [2]........................ A-level exams.

Friend: Thanks. I'll need it!

You: [3]............................... too hard.

Friend: I'll try not to.

You: [4].............................. holiday.

Father: Thanks, I'm sure we will. Give our
              regards to your parents.

You: [5] ....
              And you must [6] ....
              some time.

Mother: That's very kind of you.

You: Bye!

Friend: Bye!

What's wrong?

11 Circle and correct the mistakes.

I offe(r)ed to help her.
I offered to help her.

1 It's to hot to go for a walk.

   ....

2 You promised doing the shopping.

   ....

3 – Good luck!
   – Thanks. Same you.

   ....

4 I avoid to go to the pool on Saturdays.

   ....

5 It isn't enough warm to go in the sea.

   ....

Boost your Writing 8

1 Which is correct? Choose the correct alternative.

I've finished to do my homework.

(I've finished doing my homework.)

1 a) I enjoyed to stay in Norwich.

  b) I enjoyed staying in Norwich.

2 a) You made me feel at home.

  b) You made me to feel at home.

3 a) The time seemed to go so quickly.

  b) The time seemed going so quickly.

4 a) I want to thank you.

  b) I want thank you.

2 Read the letter and check your answers to Exercise 1.

Sonia has just spent two weeks on an exchange visit to England at the house of her penfriend, Joanna.

2 Axenstrasse
6440 Brunnen
Switzerland
24th August

Dear Mr and Mrs Harris,

I've just finished doing my homework and I'm writing to say how much I enjoyed staying in Norwich. Before I arrived, I was a little bit nervous about spending two weeks in a foreign country, but you and Joanna made me feel at home immediately. The time seemed to go so quickly.

I want to thank you again for taking me out on so many trips. It was really good of you to spend your weekends showing me the sights of Cambridge.

Please give my regards to your neighbours, Mr and Mrs Goodman. They were so kind to me when I lost my key.

If you ever felt like visiting Switzerland, you would be very welcome to stay with us here in Brunnen.
We could take you to see some of the sights here.
Come in winter and we can go skiing!

Take care,

Best wishes,

Sonia

3 Complete the sentences with the correct form of the verb. Use the letter in Exercise 2 to help you.

I was a little bit nervous about (be) *being* in a foreign country.

1 I want to thank you for (take) .... me to London.

2 It was really good of you to spend your weekends (show) .... me the countryside.

3 If you ever felt like (come) .... to France ...

4 You would be very welcome (stay) .... with my family.

5 We could take you (visit) .... some of the sights here.

4 Write a thank-you letter to your penfriend's parents. Don't forget your address and the date. Use Sonia's letter as a model.

• You spent two weeks with them in St Ives in Cornwall.

• You were a bit nervous about having to speak English all the time.

• You had a great time.

• They took you out in their boat at the weekends. They taught you how to sail.

• Their neighbours, Mr and Mrs Smart, helped you when you fell over.

• You'd like to invite your penfriend's parents to your country.

Mystery flight

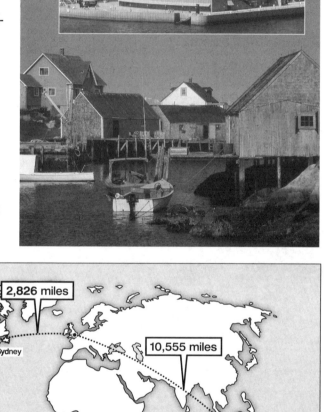

Friends Raoul Sebastian and Emma Nunn, both 19 and from London, were looking forward to their three-week holiday in Sydney, Australia.

Their Air Canada plane took off from London with no problems, but when they landed at Halifax, Nova Scotia, in Canada, and were transferred to a small 25-seat propeller plane, Emma was slightly worried. She thought the plane was taking an unusual route.
'I'm not the best flyer in the world and I said I really couldn't imagine how such a small plane could go all the way to Australia. On the plane, immigration forms were handed out. We were asked how long we were planning to stay in Canada. I told the stewardess it would only be a couple of hours. She looked surprised, but she told us to write "two hours".'

It was only when they landed at Sydney on Cape Breton Island, Nova Scotia, a town with a population of 26,000, that they finally realised their mistake. The journey had taken them just over ten hours instead of 22.

While Raoul and Emma's friends were waiting to meet them at Sydney airport in Australia, Raoul and Emma landed in Sydney on the opposite side of the world. They had booked their plane tickets on the Internet, and had chosen the wrong Sydney!

Sydney, Nova Scotia, is a small town and is not a popular tourist destination. Its main tourist sights are a park and an old house, although the countryside on the island is beautiful. Alexander Graham Bell, the inventor of the telephone, who died on Cape Breton in 1922, said, 'I have seen the Rockies, the Andes and the Alps and the Highlands of Scotland, but for simple beauty, Cape Breton is the best of them all.'

In Britain, the Association of British Travel Agents said the story was a good advertisement for using travel agents. A spokesman said, 'That's the problem with the Internet – there isn't a person in the middle.'

The story has a happy ending. Sydney, Nova Scotia, needs to attract tourists. The town used to produce steel and coal, but the industries closed down recently, so the tourism department was very pleased to have the publicity. And what happened to Raoul and Emma? They were shown the sights of Sydney, Nova Scotia and then they were given free plane tickets to Sydney, Australia.

Comprehension

Stay cool

1 Complete the chart.

Names	Raoul Sebastian and Emma Nunn
Ages	....
Home town	....
Length of holiday	....
Airline	....
The place they wanted to go to	....
The place they arrived in	....

Move on

2 Number the events in the correct order to summarise Raoul and Emma's story.

.... They arrived in Halifax, Nova Scotia.

.... They arrived in Sydney, Nova Scotia.

..*1*.. They booked their tickets.

.... They completed their immigration forms.

.... They flew to Sydney, Australia.

.... They knew that they had arrived in the wrong place.

.... They left London.

Go for it

3 Answer the questions.

What does Emma think about flying?
She doesn't really like it.

1 Why did Emma and Raoul arrive in Canada rather than Australia?

....

2 What is Sydney, Nova Scotia like as a tourist destination?

....

3 Why was the Association of British Travel Agents pleased?

....

4 Why was the tourism department of Nova Scotia pleased?

....

5 Why were Raoul and Emma pleased?

....

Communication

4 At the end of their short stay in Nova Scotia, Raoul phoned the Nova Scotia tourism department. Complete the conversation.

Raoul: Hello. Could I speak to the manager, please?

Assistant: *I'm afraid* she's out.

1 ....?

Raoul: Yes, please. Can you tell her that Raoul and Emma phoned?

Assistant: Yes, of course. Oh, wait a moment, here she is now.

Manager: Hi, Raoul! I hope you've enjoyed your time here in Nova Scotia.

Raoul: 2 ....

Manager: What did you enjoy most?

Raoul: 3 ....

Manager: I'm sorry it wasn't the place you expected to see!

Raoul: 4 ....

Manager: I hope you have a good time in the other Sydney.

Raoul: 5 ....

Assistant: Have a good trip!

Raoul: 6 ....

Writing

5 When Emma and Raoul finally reached Sydney, Australia, Emma wrote an e-mail to a friend back in London, describing what had happened. In your notebook, imagine what she wrote, using the notes below. Try to include the linkers *first, then, but, and, finally*.

We left London two weeks ago. We were really looking forward to our trip, but it wasn't quite the trip we had imagined.

The Grammar Builder

Welcome to the Grammar Builder!

- The Grammar Builder gives extensive and more detailed practice of the grammar points in the *Snapshot* course.

- The units in this section can be used alongside the units in the **Workbook** section, or for extra revision at a later stage.

- Each unit begins with a short grammar reference section called *Grammar highlights*. This gives further examples of the structures which are presented in the Students' Book. It also includes helpful additional notes.

- The practice exercises which follow the *Grammar highlights* are clearly labelled so that you know exactly which grammar point you are practising in each exercise.

1 Do you live here?

Remember....

Grammar highlights

Present simple for routines

I come here every year.
What do they do in their free time?
Do you like jazz?
Yes, I do. / No, I don't.
She doesn't usually teach at my school.
Does she work in London?
Yes, she does. / No, she doesn't.

- One use of the present simple is to talk about permanent situations and routines, e.g. *He works in a bank. She usually stays with me in the summer.*

- Adverbs of frequency come before the main verb, but after the verb *be*, e.g. *He always arrives late. He is usually late.*

- Adverbial phrases of frequency come after the verb and the object, e.g. *We see her twice a week.*

Present continuous

I'm living in a hostel at the moment.
Who are you waiting for?
Is he working this week?
Yes, he is. / No, he isn't.
Why are they laughing?
They aren't laughing.

- One use of the present continuous is to talk about things which are happening at the time of speaking or in the current period, e.g. *He's lying in the sun at the moment. She's staying with her aunt this summer.*

- The following verbs are not normally used in the continuous form: *see, hear, notice, recognise, like, love, want, hate, know, mean, mind, believe, forget, remember.*

- It is not necessary to repeat the subject in a list of verbs in the present simple or present continuous, e.g. *He lives in Brighton, works in Lewes and goes to Bristol every weekend. I'm lying in the sun, drinking a milkshake and listening to the birds.*

Echo questions

She's visiting relatives at the moment.
Is she? I am, too.

She bought it last week.
Did she? It's lovely.

- We use echo questions to show interest or surprise.

Infinitive of purpose

Are you here to improve your English?
He isn't doing it to earn money; he's doing it to meet people.

- We can express a positive purpose by using an infinitive + *to*, e.g. *I'm doing exercises to get fit.*

● **Present simple and present continuous**

1 Circle the correct answers and complete the sentences.

My grandmother always __goes__ to sleep in front of the TV.

a) (goes) b) is going   c) go

1 He .... a lot of money on clothes.

a) isn't usually spending
b) doesn't usually spend
c) usually isn't spending

2 .... this dictionary at the moment, or can I take it for a minute?

a) Do you use   b) Does he use
c) Are you using

3 .... when you're doing the washing-up?

a) Are you singing   b) You sing
c) Do you sing

4 My parents .... around China at the moment.

a) are travelling   b) travel   c) don't travel

5 My grandmother's tired, so she .... breakfast in bed today.

a) has   b) doesn't have   c) 's having

6 I often .... Josie at the sports club.

a) seeing   b) see   c) am seeing

7 .... usually drive to Cornwall in the summer?

a) Does she   b) Is she   c) Are they

8 I can't help you right now. I .... the ironing for my mum.

a) do   b) 'm doing   c) doing

● **Present simple and present continuous**

2 Use the prompts to write sentences in the present simple or the present continuous.

Snoopy's outside. He (look) for his ball.
Snoopy's outside. He's looking for his ball.

1 It never (snow) in Guatemala.

....
....

2 Please take the dog out. He really (need) to go for a walk.

....
....

3 They (have) a coffee at Carlton's at the moment. They always (have) one there after their dance class.

....
....

4 Look at this picture of Jennifer. She (wear) a crazy hat.

....
....

5 What time (she usually) get home from college?

....
....

6 Karen and Paul (stay) in a students' hostel at the moment.

....
....

7 Please can you turn the light on? I (try) to read and I can't see anything.

....
....

8 Do you want my pizza? I (not eat) it because I'm not very hungry.

....
....

Practice

● **Present simple and present continuous**

3 Complete the e-mail, putting the verbs in brackets into the present simple or present continuous.

New ▾ | Reply | Reply All | Forward | Flag | Print | Delete | Send & Receive ▾ | Address Book | Find

Outbox			subject ⬍ starts with ⬍

	To	Subject	Sent
	Tara	Florida!	

Dear Tara,

I **'m having** (have) a fantastic time in Florida. I ¹........................ (stay) with my aunt and uncle and two cousins. I ²............ (have got) a long list of books to read before next term, but I ³................................. (not read) any of them! In fact I ⁴........................ (not use) my brain at all! Instead I ⁵........................... (get) a tan and I ⁶........................ (study) the art of total relaxation!

Right now I ⁷........................ (sit) in the garden with my feet in the swimming pool. I ⁸........................ (drink) a big chocolate milkshake. The sun ⁹........................... (shine) and the birds ¹⁰........................ (sing).

Every day we ¹¹............ (go) to the beach. I ¹²........................ (learn) to water ski. I'm not very good yet and I often ¹³............ (fall) over but it's fun. Sometimes I ¹⁴............ (borrow) my cousins' jet-ski. It's brilliant fun but the jet-ski ¹⁵............ (make) a terrible noise. I'm afraid the people on the beach ¹⁶........................ (not like) it.

The food here is great. I ¹⁷.................... (get) fat because it's so delicious. I usually ¹⁸.................... (have) a milkshake and ice cream for breakfast! We ¹⁹........................ (not eat) a big lunch – usually just sandwiches and fruit salad. In the evenings my uncle always ²⁰............ (have) a barbecue. I ²¹.................... (love) the hamburgers and sausages here. ²²................................. (you/have) a nice time in Cambridge? Is your job at Patsy's Pizzas OK? What time ²³...................... (you/start) work every day? ²⁴................... (you/get) a free lunch at the restaurant? ²⁵...................................... (Martin/work) hard for his exams? Write soon and tell me all your news.

Love,

Phil

● **Echo questions**

4 Write responses using echo questions.

A: My computer crashes all the time.

B: *Does it?* Mine works perfectly.

1 A: I usually walk to school.

   B: .... ? I usually get a lift with my father.

2 A: Sara and Joey have got a sweet little dog.

   B: .... ? We haven't got any pets.

3 A: Julia lives in Spain now.

   B: .... ? In which city?

4 A: My grandmother is buying a motorbike.

   B: .... ? I hope she doesn't drive too fast!

5 A: Ella's got three older brothers.

   B: .... ? How old are they?

6 A: They're buying a house in California.

   B: .... ? I hope I can go and stay with them.

7 A: John's working at the swimming pool.

   B: .... ? What does he have to do?

8 A: These shoes hurt my feet.

   B: .... ? Mine are really comfortable.

9 A: I've got tickets to the match on Saturday.

   B: .... ? I couldn't get any.

● Infinitive of purpose

5 Match the sentence halves and write the complete sentences.

He's wearing a jacket ...   `d`

1 We're going to the beach ...   ☐
2 I'm going to Rome for six months ...   ☐
3 She's using the computer ...   ☐
4 Did you buy that top ...   ☐
5 How many hours did you train ...   ☐
6 Which shoe shop do you go to ...   ☐

a) ... to buy your trainers?
b) ... to get so fit?
c) ... to have a swim.
d) ... to keep warm.
e) ... to learn Italian.
f) ... to wear to Becky's party?
g) ... to write her History project.

He's wearing a jacket to keep warm.

1 ....
   ....
2 ....
   ....
3 ....
   ....
4 ....
   ....
5 ....
   ....
6 ....
   ....

● Infinitive of purpose

6 Write sentences using an infinitive of purpose.

He wants to go travelling. That's why he's bought a rucksack.

He's bought a rucksack to go travelling.

1 She wanted to listen to the news. That's why she turned the radio on.
   ....
   ....

2 I want to keep fit. That's why I go running every day.
   ....
   ....

3 We were visiting our cousins. That's why we went to Ireland.
   ....
   ....

4 She wants to buy a motorbike. That's why she's saving money.
   ....
   ....

5 She needs to get dollars for her trip. That's why she's gone to the bank.
   ....
   ....

6 They want to talk about the play. That's why they're meeting next week.
   ....
   ....

7 I wanted to have a check-up. That's why I went to the doctor.
   ....
   ....

8 He wants to read the letter. That's why he's putting on his glasses.
   ....
   ....

9 He's inviting them to a party. That's why he's e-mailing his friends.
   ....
   ....

2 Over three hours late.

Remember....

Grammar highlights

Past simple
We arrived late.
She left early.
They didn't stay.
Did you meet your friend?
Yes, I did. / No, I didn't.
Who did you talk to?
Didn't you meet anyone?
They arrived last week.
I met her this summer.
Didn't she phone this morning?

- The past simple positive form of regular verbs ends in *-ed*. In most cases, we add *-ed* to the infinitive: *climb/climbed,* but:
  — if the infinitive ends in *-e*, we add *-d*: *arrive/arrived; die/died.*
  — if the infinitive ends in a consonant + *y*, we delete the *y* and add *-ied*: *study/studied; cry/cried.*
  — if the infinitive ends in a stressed syllable of one vowel and one consonant (not *y* or *w*), we double the consonant: *trip/tripped; step/stepped.* Note: There are some exceptions, e.g. *travel/travelled.*
- There is a list of irregular verbs at the back of this book.

- We make questions with *did* + infinitive and negative statements with *didn't* + infinitive.

- We often use time adverbials with the past simple, e.g. *I arrived an hour ago.*
- We say *in the morning/ afternoon/evening* but *at night*.
- We do not use prepositions in time adverbials if we are using the demonstrative pronoun *this*, e.g. *They arrived this morning.* (**not** *They arrived in this morning.*)

Conjunctions *so* and *because*
I was tired so I went to bed.
I went to bed because I was tired.

- We use *so* to talk about a consequence and *because* to talk about a reason.

Linkers
*first (of all), then,
before (breakfast), after (that),
later, the next day, in the end*

● Past simple: positive forms

1 Complete the passage, putting the verbs in brackets in the past simple.

Last summer I _went_ (go) to stay with my grandmother in Australia. The flight ¹................. (be) at nine in the morning, but I ²................ (have) to be at the airport by seven. My mother ³................. (wake) me up at five and ⁴................. (give) me a cup of tea. Then I ⁵................. (get up), ⁶................. (run) downstairs and ⁷................. (make) myself a sandwich to eat in the car on the way to the airport. My father ⁸................. (drive), and on the way, my mother ⁹................. (ask) me annoying questions every five minutes, like 'Have you got your passport, darling?' and 'What time do you get to Sydney?' I ¹⁰................. (answer) her questions and ¹¹................. (try) not to feel nervous about the journey. When we ¹²................. (arrive) at the airport, I ¹³................. (show) the man my passport and ticket, ¹⁴................. (say) goodbye to my parents and ¹⁵................. (wait) to get on the plane. At last I ¹⁶................. (hear) the announcement and we all ¹⁷................. (walk) to Gate Number 9. The plane was very full, and I was the last person to get on. There was already someone in my seat, so the flight attendant ¹⁸................. (tell) me to go and sit in first class. I ¹⁹................. (follow) her to my new seat in first class and guess what? Kylie Minogue was in the seat next to me.

● Past simple: all forms

2 Write questions and answers in the past simple.

Q: Why (she get) angry?
A: Because I (forget) to meet her at the cinema.
Q: _Why did she get angry?_
A: _Because I forgot to meet her at the cinema._

1 Q: How much (you pay) for your bike?
A: I (not pay) anything. My brother (give) it to me.
Q: ....
A: ....
....
....

2 Q: Who (take) the last packet of crisps?
A: Joey. He also (drink) all the orange juice.
Q: ....
A: ....
....
....

3 Q: (Kerry lose) your mobile phone?
A: No, she (lose) my camera. But she (buy) me a new one.
Q: ....
A: ....
....
....

4 Q: (she draw) a map for us?
A: She (draw) one this morning and (leave) it on the table for you.
Q: ....
A: ....
....
....

5 Q: What you (do) in Edinburgh?
A: We (go) to the castle. I'm sure I (see) a ghost there.
Q: ....
A: ....
....
....

Practice

- **Past simple**
- **Linkers**

3 Complete the passage, putting the verbs in brackets in the past simple and filling in the blanks a) to d) with the linkers in the box.

- Then • Later • ~~First of all~~ • After
- The next day

Last year we **_spent_** (spend) two weeks camping on St Agnes, one of the Scilly Isles, off the coast of Cornwall. It ¹............ (be) a very long and tiring journey to get there. **_First of all_** we ²............ (take) a taxi to Paddington station at five in the morning. ᵃ⁾_____ we ³............ (catch) the train to Penzance, in Cornwall. ᵇ⁾_____ that, we ⁴............ (walk) from Penzance station to the docks. At Penzance docks we ⁵............ (get) a ferry to an island called St Mary's. Unfortunately, the sea ⁶............ (be) very rough and we ⁷............ (be) all sick on the ferry. When we ⁸............ (arrive) at St Mary's, we ⁹............ (go) to a café to relax. ᶜ⁾_____ , when we ¹⁰............ (feel) better, we ¹¹............ (take) a small boat to St Agnes. The campsite owner ¹²............ (meet) us at St Agnes quay and ¹³............ (give) us a lift to the campsite on his tractor. We ¹⁴............ (put) up our tents and ¹⁵............ (go) to bed early. ᵈ⁾_____ we ¹⁶............ (sleep) really late.

- **Past simple**
- **Conjunction** _because_

4 Match the sentence halves. Then write the sentences in the past simple with _because_.

He (go) to singing classes ... | c |

1 I (get) up at four this morning ... ☐
2 She (think) about him all day ... ☐
3 I (borrow) some money ... ☐
4 They (stop) and (put) their tent up ... ☐
5 She (have) a hot bath ... ☐
6 They (give) me a book about Thailand ... ☐
7 He (find) a new job ... ☐

a) ... he (not like) working in the shop.
b) ... I (not know) anything about the place.
c) ... he (want) to be in a musical.
d) ... I (can't) sleep.
e) ... she (like) him a lot.
f) ... I (not have) any in my purse.
g) ... she (feel) cold and tired.
h) ... they (be) tired after cycling all day.

He went to singing classes because he
wanted to be in a musical.

1 ....
   ....
   ....

2 ....
   ....
   ....

3 ....
   ....
   ....

4 ....
   ....
   ....

5 ....
   ....
   ....

6 ....
   ....
   ....

7 ....
   ....
   ....

- Past simple
- Conjunction *so*

5 Rewrite the sentences in Exercise 4 using *so*.

He wanted to be in a musical so he went to singing classes.

1 ....
....
....

2 ....
....
....

3 ....
....
....

4 ....
....
....

5 ....
....
....

6 ....
....
....

7 ....
....
....

- Past simple
- Conjunctions *so* and *because*

6 Write sentences with *so* or *because*, putting the verbs in brackets in the past simple.

A beautiful bird (fly) into the garden; I (take) a picture of it.

A beautiful bird flew into the garden, so I took a picture of it.

1 I (break) my arm; I (can't) compete in the tennis championship.
....
....

2 I (stay) up all night; I (feel) terrible the next day.
....
....

3 He (break) the lamp; he (pay) for a new one.
....
....

4 She (buy) a tent; she (want) to go camping.
....
....

5 We (find) a purse in the street; we (take) it to the police station.
....
....

6 I (call) from a phone box; I (not have) my mobile with me.
....
....

7 We (walk) out of the concert; it (be) really boring.
....
....

3 A view which excites me.

Grammar highlights

Defining relative clauses with *who, which, where*

The girl who lives next door is Australian.
Where is the money which was on the table?
I know a place where you can get cheap CDs.

- Defining relative clauses give essential information. They do not have commas.

Non-defining relative clauses with *who, which, where*

Jim, who loves cooking, made that cake.
Strawberries, which are my favourite fruit, are delicious with sugar and fresh cream.
I often go to stay in Penzance, which is a busy seaside town in Cornwall.
Penzance, where my friend Georgia lives, is a busy seaside town.

- Non-defining relative clauses, which give extra information and which can be left out, have a comma before the relative clause and a comma or full stop after it.

- In relative clauses, we use *who* to refer to people, *which* to refer to things and *where* to refer to places.

- In defining relative clauses, we can also use *that* to refer to people and things, e.g. *He's got a jacket that cost £200.*

Future with *going to*

I'm going to walk.
We aren't going to take the bus.
Are you going to buy a new bike?
Yes, I am. / No, I'm not.
Isn't Lucy going to give us a lift?

- We use *going to* to talk about intentions, e.g. *'There's no milk.' 'Yes, I know. I'm going to buy some.'*

- We also use *going to* for predictions about the immediate future, particularly when we already have evidence of what is going to happen, e.g. *Look at those clouds. It's going to rain.*

Future with *will/won't*

I'll (will) be back soon. (promise)
Jim won't (will not) be late. (prediction)
You'll (will) be sorry. (threat)
OK, we'll (will) leave tomorrow. (decision)
Will there be a night bus?
Yes, there will. / No, there won't.
Won't it be dangerous to cycle in the dark?

- We use *will/won't* for predictions, promises, threats and decisions. We also use *will/won't* to give opinions after verbs like *be sure, think, know* and *hope.*

Future with present continuous

We're seeing him tomorrow.
They aren't coming on Sunday.
Are you working next week?
Yes, I am. / No, I'm not.
Aren't they getting married this July?

- We use the present continuous to talk about definite future arrangements. This tense is common with time phrases, e.g. *I'm seeing Jim tomorrow.*

• Relative clauses

1 Complete the sentences with *who, which* or *where*. Add commas where necessary.

The Best of LONDON

The London Eye, ...*which*... takes thirty minutes to go round, will give you an amazing view of the city.

1 Tate Modern is the art gallery .... you can see the most exciting modern art.

2 The Tower .... is London's most popular tourist attraction was built in the twelfth century.

3 Big Ben is the clock .... every visitor wants to photograph.

4 Covent Garden .... musicians and actors perform at weekends is very popular with tourists.

5 People .... are interested in fashion will love the clothes at Portobello Market.

6 In London, there are parks .... you can swim, ride horses or have boat rides.

7 Camden Market .... you can shop, eat or look at people is a great place to go on Saturday or Sunday.

8 The writer Samuel Johnson .... was born in 1709 said, 'When a man is tired of London, he is tired of life'.

• Future with present continuous

2 Use the verbs in the box in the present continuous to complete the dialogue.

• do • give • go • have • help
• leave • ~~look after~~ • make • play
• take • work

Mike: Would you like to come to the cinema with me tomorrow night?

Jade: I can't, Mike. I'm ___*looking after*___ my little brother. My parents [1]................... to a concert.

Mike: What [2]................... you .... on Saturday morning?

Jade: I [3]....................... tennis with Sandra, and then we [4].......................... lunch at her house.

Mike: [5]....................................... on Saturday afternoon?

Jade: No, I'm not. I haven't got a Saturday job any more. This Saturday, Sandra and I [6].................................... a cake for my sister.

Mike: Oh, yes, it's her birthday on Sunday. What [7]................... you .... her?

Jade: Some earrings and some perfume. My parents [8].......................... us all out to dinner at a Chinese restaurant on Sunday.

Mike: Lucky you! Are you free on Monday evening?

Jade: Not really. I [9]..................... Miss Lewis with the school art exhibition. Why don't you come and help, too?

Mike: OK.

Jade: Meet me at my place and we can walk to school together.

Mike: Sure. What time [10]........................ you .... your house?

Jade: About six thirty.

Mike: OK. See you then.

Practice

• **Future with *'ll (will)/won't***

3 Write questions and answers, using the verbs in brackets with *'ll (will)/won't*.

   Q: When (you / phone) me?

   A: I (phone) tomorrow. I (not forget)

   Q: *When will you phone me?*

   A: *I'll phone tomorrow. I won't forget.*

1 **Q:** What time (you / get) back?

    A: We (be) back by midnight. We (not be) late.

    Q: ....

    ....

    A: ....

    ....

2 **Q:** How (they / get) home from the club?

    A: There (not be) any buses so they (have) to get a taxi.

    Q: ....

    ....

    A: ....

    ....

3 **Q:** (you / write) to me soon?

    A: I (not write) but I (phone) you from Paris.

    Q: ....

    ....

    A: ....

    ....

4 **Q:** (you / have) a drink?

    A: I (not have) a drink, thanks. I (have) a sandwich.

    Q: ....

    ....

    A: ....

    ....

5 **Q:** What (the weather / be) like?

    A: It (not be) hot. It (rain), I think.

    Q: ....

    ....

    A: ....

    ....

• **Future with present continuous**
• **Future with *'ll (will)/won't***

4 Write sentences, putting the verbs in brackets in the present continuous or the future with *'ll/won't*.

That box looks heavy. I (help) you with it.

That box looks heavy. I'll help you with it.

1 Don't forget. You (see) the doctor at four o'clock tomorrow.

   ....

   ....

2 Anna and Sam (have) a beach party on Saturday.

   ....

   ....

3 I know I (forget) everything in the exam and I (not write) anything.

   ....

   ....

4 '(you / do) anything tonight?' 'Yes. We (go) to a concert at the Albert Hall.'

   ....

   ....

5 'Where (you / wait) for me?' 'I (meet) you outside the cinema.'

   ....

   ....

6 You can tell Martin your secret. He (not repeat) it.

   ....

   ....

7 He can't come tomorrow. He (go) to Bristol.

   ....

   ....

- Future with *going to*
- Future with present continuous

5 Complete the conversation, putting the verbs in brackets in the present continuous if possible. If it is not possible, use *going to*.

Kate: Do you want to play tennis with me on Friday evening?

Jamie: I can't. **I'm helping** (I/help) my sister with her room. [1].............................. (She/change) everything in it, and [2]........................... (I/paint) it for her.

Kate: [3]..................................... (you/choose) the colours?

Jamie: No, she is. She wants it red and purple.

Kate: Red and purple? [4].............................. .... (your parents/be) happy about that?

Jamie: [5]........................ (They/go) to Italy on Friday, so they [6].............................. (not/see) the new colours for a week. [7]..................................... (They/come) home on the 23rd. And [8]...................... .... (they/get) a very big surprise. [9].................................. (They/think) they're in the wrong house!

Kate: What [10].............................. (you/do) tonight? Anything exciting?

Jamie: [11]............................ (I/stay) at home. [12].................................... (I/go) to bed early and [13]..................................... (I/dream) about pots of paint and strange colours!

- Future with *will/won't*
- Future with *going to*

6 Match the pairs of sentences. Complete each second sentence with *'ll/won't* or *going to* and write it in the correct space.

I'm not going to their party. $\boxed{g}$
I'm sure I won't enjoy it.
....

1 Why is Andy holding his car keys? □
....
....

2 Have a great holiday. □
....
....

3 I can't do this Maths problem. □
....
....

4 Are you going to the beach with Naomi? □
....
....

5 Why are David and Angela always so happy? □
....
....

6 What are you doing with my bike? □
....
....

7 What are you doing with that paint? □
....
....

8 Why is Adam holding a video? □
....
....

a) (He/take) it back to the shop.
b) (I/fix) it for you.
c) (He/drive) us to college.
d) No. (It/be) too cold for a swim.
e) (They/get) married in May.
f) Don't worry. (I/help) you with it.
g) I'm sure (I/not enjoy) it.
h) (I/paint) my bedroom green.
i) Thanks. (I/see) you in September.

4 How long have you been here?

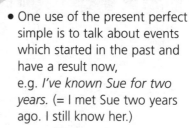

Remember....

Grammar highlights

Present perfect simple with *for* and *since*

She's been here for an hour.
She's been here since one o'clock.
Have you worked here for a long time?
Yes, I have. / No, I haven't.
How long have you known Jim?
I've known him for two months.
I've known him since July.
I haven't seen him for a week.

- One use of the present perfect simple is to talk about events which started in the past and have a result now, e.g. *I've known Sue for two years.* (= I met Sue two years ago. I still know her.)
- When we use the present perfect simple tense, we use *for* to talk about a period of time, e.g. *three hours*, and *since* to talk about a point in time, e.g. *last Wednesday*.

Comparison of adjectives

Short adjectives

strong	stronger	strongest
fit	fitter	fittest
happy	happier	happiest

Long adjectives

important	more important	most important

Irregular adjectives

good	better	best
bad	worse	worst
far	further	furthest

Comparative

The beach is more crowded today than yesterday.
It's usually hotter in August than in July.

Superlative

She's one of the best surfers in Cornwall.
It's the most exciting sport I've ever done.

- We form the comparative of short adjectives (not ending in *y*) by adding -*er* or -*r*, and the superlative by adding -*est* or -*st*, e.g. *strong, stronger, strongest; large, larger, largest*.
- When an adjective has one or two syllables and ends in *y*, we usually form the comparative and superlative by deleting the *y* and adding -*ier*/-*iest*, e.g. *funny, funnier, funniest*.
- When an adjective has one syllable and ends in one vowel and one consonant, we double the final consonant in the comparative and superlative, e.g. *fit, fitter, fittest*.
- To form the comparative and superlative of long adjectives, we put *more* or *most* in front of the adjective, e.g. *more independent, most independent*.

Intensifier *much* + comparative adjective

He's much healthier than his brother.

- We can use the intensifier *much* to make a comparative stronger.

Comparison with *(not) as ... as*

This CD isn't as good as her first one.
My bike was just as expensive as yours.
Is the water as cold as it was yesterday?

- We can also use *as ... as* with *almost, nearly* or *just*, e.g. *The beach is almost as crowded as it was yesterday.*

● **Present perfect simple with *for* and *since***

1 Use the prompts to write questions in the present perfect and answers with *for* or *since*.

Q: Annabel / be / an actress
A: two years
Q: *How long has Annabel been an actress?*
A: *She's been an actress for two years.*

1 **Q:** she / have / a mobile phone?
  A: three months
  Q: ....
  A: ....

2 **Q:** you / know / Steve?
  A: December
  Q: ....
  A: ....

3 **Q:** your grandmother / live / in Australia
  A: 1995
  Q: ....
  A: ....

4 **Q:** you / have / that black eye?
  A: more than a week
  Q: ....
  A: ....

5 **Q:** that café / be / open
  A: three days
  Q: ....
  A: ....

6 **Q:** you work / at the bookshop
  A: 21st January
  Q: ....
  A: ....

● **Present perfect simple with *for* and *since***

2 Complete the e-mail, putting the verbs in brackets in the present perfect and filling blanks a) to i) with *for* or *since*.

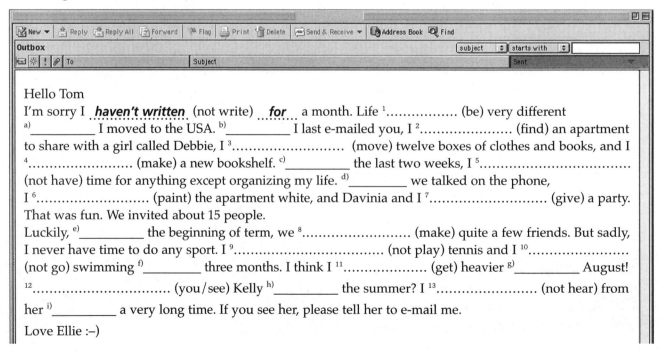

Hello Tom

I'm sorry I __haven't written__ (not write) __for__ a month. Life ¹................. (be) very different
a)_____ I moved to the USA. b)_____ I last e-mailed you, I ²..................... (find) an apartment
to share with a girl called Debbie, I ³.......................... (move) twelve boxes of clothes and books, and I
⁴........................ (make) a new bookshelf. c)_____ the last two weeks, I ⁵..................................
(not have) time for anything except organizing my life. d)_____ we talked on the phone,
I ⁶.......................... (paint) the apartment white, and Davinia and I ⁷.......................... (give) a party.
That was fun. We invited about 15 people.
Luckily, e)_____ the beginning of term, we ⁸.......................... (make) quite a few friends. But sadly,
I never have time to do any sport. I ⁹.................................. (not play) tennis and I ¹⁰.......................
(not go) swimming f)_____ three months. I think I ¹¹................... (get) heavier g)_____ August!
¹²................................. (you/see) Kelly h)_____ the summer? I ¹³........................ (not hear) from
her i)_____ a very long time. If you see her, please tell her to e-mail me.
Love Ellie :–)

● **Comparative and superlative adjectives**

3 Look at the sports club guide. Write a comparative and a superlative sentence for each word or phrase.

Fitness First _is newer than_ The Spring.

The Village Gym _is the newest_ .

1 Fitness First ....
the Village Gym.

The Spring ....

2 Fitness First ....
the Village Gym.

The Spring ....

3 The Spring has ....
the Village Gym.

Fitness First has ....

4 The Spring has ....
Fitness First.

The Village Gym has ....

5 The Spring has ....
Fitness First.

The Village Gym has ....

● Intensifier _much/a bit_ + comparative adjective
● Comparison with _just as/not as … as_

4 Use the prompts to make comparisons with _much/a bit_ + comparative adjective or _just as/not as_ + adjective.

today (38°C) / yesterday (28°C) (hot)

Today's much hotter than yesterday.

today (33°C) / yesterday (32°C) (hot)

Today's a bit hotter than yesterday.

today (30°C) / yesterday (30°C) (hot)

Today's just as hot as yesterday.

today (27°C) / yesterday (31°C) (hot)

Today's not as hot as yesterday.

1 Racehorses (72km per hour) / cheetahs (69km per hour) / (fast)

....

....

2 Michael Jordan (£25 million per year) / David Beckham (£9 million) (well-paid)

....

....

3 Sumatran rhinos (about 200 left) / giant pandas (about 200 left) (endangered)

....

....

4 Andrea (1m 70) / Serena (1m 75) (tall)

....

....

5 Blue whales (120 tonnes) / elephants (5.2 tonnes) (heavy)

....

....

6 A Zeta watch (£35) / a Romeo watch (£33) (expensive)

....

....

7 The Amazon (6,400km) / the Nile (6,600km) (short)

....

....

6 They were exploring the glacier.

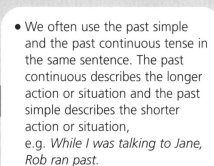

Grammar highlights

Past simple and past continuous with time markers *while, as, when*

While I was swimming, somebody stole my clothes.
I was watching TV when I heard a scream.
As we were talking, the lights went out.
He wasn't going fast when his car hit the tree.
What was she wearing when you saw her?
Was she wearing a hat when you saw her?

- We often use the past simple and the past continuous tense in the same sentence. The past continuous describes the longer action or situation and the past simple describes the shorter action or situation,
  e.g. *While I was talking to Jane, Rob ran past.*

- Clauses in the past continuous are often introduced by *while* and *as*. Clauses in the past simple are often introduced by *when*.

- When the *while*, *when* or *as* clause comes first, it is followed by a comma.

Prepositions of motion

across, along, from, towards, through, past, into, over, under, up, down

● **Past continuous or past simple**

1 **Put the verbs in brackets in the past continuous or past simple.**

She (wait) to pay for her shopping when somebody (steal) her purse.

She was waiting to pay for her shopping ......

when somebody stole her purse. ......

1 How fast (he / drive) when he (hit) the other car?

......
......

2 The phone (ring) while we (watch) a programme about surfing.

......
......

3 As she (get) ready to dive, somebody (push) her in.

......
......

4 I (not go) very fast when I (fall) off my motorbike.

......
......

5 When you (pull) her out of the water, (she / breathe)?

......
......

6 (you / live) in Spain when you (meet) your girlfriend?

......
......

7 As they (leave) the beach, they suddenly (hear) a scream.

......
......

8 She (drown) when he suddenly (see) her and (rescue) her.

......
......

9 He (take) my bag while I (not look).

......
......

● **Past continuous or past simple**

2 **Complete the passage, putting the verbs in brackets in the correct tense: past simple or past continuous.**

Last summer I _went_ (go) to stay with a friend in Scotland. Her family lives in a very old house next to a lake. One evening, while my friend [1]...................... (talk) on the phone and her parents [2]............................... (watch) television, I [3].................... (decide) to go for a walk around the lake. I [4]............................... (walk) down the stairs from my room when I [5]............... (see) a girl in a long, white dress. She [6]......................... (carry) an old lamp and she [7]...................... (sing) quietly. I [8].............. (smile) at her and [9].............. (say) 'Hello', but she [10]............... (walk) past me quickly. While I [11].......................... (walk) around the lake, I suddenly [12].................. (notice) a strange light in my bedroom window. I [13].......................... (look) at the window when it suddenly [14]................. (open) and I [15].............. (see) the girl from the stairs. She [16].......................... (wear) my green hat and scarf. I [17]................. (run) back to the house and [18]................. (ask) my friend about her. 'Don't worry,' she [19].............. (say). 'That girl is Dora. She [20].............. (die) in your room 100 years ago, but she sometimes comes back and tries on people's clothes. Most people don't see her. You were lucky.' Lucky? I wasn't sure about that.

6 Practice

● **Prepositions of motion**

3 Write sentences about the game, using the present simple of the verbs in brackets and a preposition from the box.

THE ULTIMATE CHALLENGE

player 1

player 2

- across - along - down - into - over - over
- ~~through~~ - through - up - up

1 the forest (cycle)

2 the river (swim)

3 Devil's Rock (climb)

4 the old bridge (go)

5 the rope ladder (climb)

6 the plastic tunnel (crawl)

7 the steps (go)

8 the wooden bar (walk)

9 the ditch (jump)

10 the Blue Lake (dive)

1 *You cycle through the forest.* ....

2 ....

3 ....

4 ....

5 ....

6 ....

7 ....

8 ....

9 ....

10 ....

7 I've just spilt coffee.

Grammar highlights

Question tags

Positive statements with negative tags

We're in trouble, aren't we?
He's got a bike, hasn't he?
She knows Rosie, doesn't she?
I told you, didn't I?
I haven't failed my exam, have I?
She can speak Chinese, can't she?
It'll be sunny tomorrow, won't it?

Negative statements with positive tags

We aren't late, are we?
They haven't got a car, have they?
They don't eat meat, do they?
You didn't find her, did you?
She hasn't seen us, has she?
He can't dive, can he?
You won't lose the money, will you?

- One use of question tags is to check information.
- We use a positive statement followed by a negative tag when we expect the answer *Yes*, e.g. *You're American, aren't you?*
- We use a negative statement followed by a positive tag when we expect the answer *No*, e.g. *They haven't arrived yet, have they?*

Present perfect simple with time adverbials *just*, *already*, *yet*

I've just seen a brilliant film.
They've already told me about it.
Mark hasn't arrived yet.
Have you spoken to Angela yet?
He's already seen *Titanic*. He saw it last month.
He's just bought a motorbike. He bought it in Brighton.
I got my new camera last week, but I haven't used it yet.

- The present perfect simple tense is often used with the words *just*, *already* and *yet*. The words *just* and *already* come between the auxiliary verb *have* and the main verb. The word *yet* comes at the end of the sentence.
- We normally use *just* and *already* in positive statements.
- We normally use *yet* in questions and negative statements.

- We use the present perfect simple tense to talk about an action in the past that has a result now. We use the past simple tense to talk about a completed action in the past.
- With past time adverbials like *ago*, *yesterday*, *last year*, *in 1989*, we use the past simple (not the present perfect simple) e.g. *I saw him a week ago.* (**not** ~~I've seen him a week ago.~~)

Past simple and present perfect simple

Laura's just got back from California. She went there two weeks ago for her cousin's wedding.

- The verb *go* has two present perfect forms: *have/has gone* and *have/has been*. We use *have/has been* when the person has made a visit and come back, e.g. *She has been to Newquay.* (= She has visited Newquay and returned.) We use *have/has gone* when the person has not returned, e.g. *He has gone to India.* (= He is in India. He isn't here.)

7 Practice

• **Question tags: positive statement, negative tag**

1 Complete the questions with the correct tag.

You live in New York, *don't you* ?

1 She's moved house, ... ?
2 They were at your old school, ...
.... ?
3 I can work at this desk, ... ?
4 He was upset, ... ?
5 I'll meet them at your party, ... ?
6 We've agreed, ... ?
7 They know the way, ... ?
8 We're coming to your house on Sunday,
.... ?
9 You told her the truth, ... ?
10 You're in my dance class, ...
.... ?
11 Your father's a doctor, ... ?
12 I know your cousin, ... ?

• **Question tags: negative statement, positive tag**

2 Complete the questions with the correct tag.

Veronica hasn't called, *has she* ?

1 You can't remember her number,
.... ?
2 This pizza isn't very nice, ... ?
3 She didn't recognise you, ... ?
4 Sally doesn't wear glasses, ... ?
5 Mark isn't interested in sport, ... ?
6 He won't lend me his bike, ... ?
7 They haven't got time today, ...
.... ?
8 You weren't at Sue's party, ... ?
9 We haven't finished the cake yet, ...
.... ?
10 We aren't meeting tomorrow, ... ?
11 They aren't going to invite us, ... ?
12 We haven't played tennis for ages, ...
.... ?
13 I'm not a great singer, ... ?
14 You don't speak Russian, ... ?

• **Question tags: positive and negative**

3 Match the sentence halves. Then write the sentences and add question tags.

Elvis Presley died ...   [e]
1 Dirk isn't ...   ☐
2 There aren't any ...   ☐
3 J.K. Rowling wrote ...   ☐
4 Spiders have got ...   ☐
5 Marilyn Monroe starred ...   ☐
6 Cats don't ...   ☐
7 Mobile phones didn't ...   ☐

a) a Spanish name.
b) in *Some Like It Hot*.
c) eight legs.
d) exist in the 1960s.
e) in 1977.
f) the Harry Potter books.
g) tigers in Africa.
h) usually like swimming.

Elvis Presley died in 1977, didn't he?

1 ....
2 ....
3 ....
4 ....
5 ....
6 ....
7 ....

104

- **Present perfect simple with *yet***

4 Write pairs of sentences using the present perfect simple + *yet* and the present continuous + *still*. Then match the sentences to the pictures.

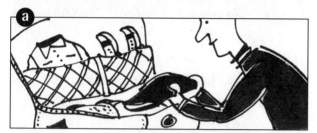

Amy (not take) her book back to the library. She (read) it.

Amy hasn't taken her book back to the library yet. She'e still reading it. ☐ *f*

1 '(you/find) a holiday job?' 'No, I (look) for one.'

....
.... ☐

2 I (not eat) my breakfast. I (do) my exercises.

....
.... ☐

3 '(you/send) an e-mail to Justin?' 'No, I (write) it.'

....
.... ☐

4 Andy (not leave) yet. He (pack) his case.

....
.... ☐

5 '(you/buy) any new shoes?' 'No, (wear) my old ones.'

....
.... ☐

6 Alex (not/paint) the room. He (move) the furniture out.

....
.... ☐

7 Wendy (not/get) in the pool. She (lie) in the sun.

....
.... ☐

● **Present perfect simple with time adverbials**
just, already, yet

5 Complete the letter. Put the verbs in brackets in the present perfect simple and write the correct time phrase if given.

Dear Michael,

Thank you very much for the card and flowers which **have just arrived** ([just/yet] arrive).
I ¹..................... (be) in hospital for ten days now but I ²..................... (not have) time to get bored ³................... [already/yet]. Most of my friends ⁴..................... (visit) me every day. In fact, Laura ⁵................... ([just/yet] leave). Lisa ⁶.......................... ([already/yet] not come) but it's hard for her as she's working AND studying at the moment. Since I ⁷................... (be) here, I ⁸..
([just/already] read) three books – long ones – and I ⁹................... (write) about sixteen letters.
Somebody ¹⁰...
([just/yet] turn on) the TV. There's an excellent comedy channel on it and there's a Mr Bean film on

at the moment. I ¹¹.................................
([just/already] see) it and I don't want to see it again, so I'll continue with this letter.
¹²........................... (you/buy) a new windsurfer ¹³........................... [just/yet]?
¹⁴........................... (Mr Jackson/give) you back the History projects?
¹⁵........................... (your brother/go) to South America ¹⁶................... [just/yet]?
¹⁷........................... (Tom/invite) Maria out ¹⁸................... [just/yet]?
Write soon and tell me all the news.
Lots of love,
Rebecca

● **Past simple and present perfect simple**

6 Put the verbs in brackets in the past simple or the present perfect simple.

Laura: *Did you see* (you see) *The Grove* yesterday?

Chloe: No, I didn't. I ¹......................... (not watch) TV for months. What ².................... .... (happen) since April? ³....................................... (Kate / have) her baby yet?

Laura: Yes. She ⁴................... (have) the baby weeks ago!

Chloe: What about Brett and Kylie? ⁵............. .... (they / start) going out yet?

Laura: Brett and Kylie ⁶..................... (not be) in *The Grove* for about a month.

Chloe: Why not?

Laura: They ⁷................. (have) a terrible car accident on Kylie's birthday and Brett ⁸................. (die).

Chloe: That's awful. What ⁹......................... (Kylie / do) after the accident?

Laura: It was really sad. After the accident, Kylie ¹⁰......................... (go) back to Australia. She ¹¹................................. (not want) to stay in England.

Chloe: ¹²......................... (Chris / leave) his wife yet?

Laura: Yes. In fact he ¹³............................. (already find) a new woman – Shirley. They ¹⁴................. (meet) on the bus!

Chloe: ¹⁵... (old Mrs Moreton / die) yet?

Laura: No. She's very happy at the moment because her son, Liam,¹⁶..................... .... (just come) back from California. Why don't you come round and watch it with me tonight?

Chloe: I haven't got time. I'll phone tomorrow for the latest news!

8 You ought to try them.

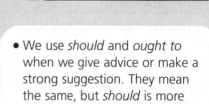

Grammar highlights

Verbs *should* and *ought to*

Positive statements
She should go to bed earlier.
You ought to write to her.

Negative statements
She shouldn't go to bed so late.
You oughtn't (ought not) to speak behind her back.

Questions
Should I tell her?
Ought we to go?
What should they do?
She should go to bed earlier, shouldn't she?

- We use *should* and *ought to* when we give advice or make a strong suggestion. They mean the same, but *should* is more common, especially in questions.

Verbs *have to* and *must/mustn't*

Positive statements
I can't talk now. I have to go to work.
I couldn't talk because I had to go to work.
I'm very tired. I must go to bed.
I was very tired. I had to go to bed.

Questions
What must we do?
Do I have to tidy my room now, Mum?
We mustn't forget our tickets, must we?
We have to write a History essay, don't we?

Negative statements
You don't have to do this work if you don't want to.
At my last school, we didn't have to wear a uniform.
We mustn't make a noise. My parents are asleep.

- In positive statements, we normally use *have to* to talk about obligations which come from other people, or from routines.
- In positive statements, we normally use *must* to express the feelings and wishes of the speaker.
- *Have to* and *must* are very close in meaning. In positive statements, if you aren't sure which to use, it's safest to use *have/has to*.
- We can't use *must* to talk about past obligations. We use *had to*.

- The negatives *mustn't* and *don't/ doesn't have to* have completely different meanings. We use *mustn't* to talk about prohibition. We use *don't/doesn't/didn't have to* to express a lack of obligation.
- In questions and negatives with *have to*, we normally use the auxiliaries *do, does, did*.

Would you mind? + gerund
Would you mind opening the window?
Would you mind not making a noise?

- **Verbs *should(n't)* and *ought(n't) to*: positive and negative**

1 Write pairs of sentences with *should(n't)* and *ought(n't) to*, using the prompts and a phrase from the box.

- buy new clothes all the time • tidy it
- close it down • start training
- go swimming yet • ~~go to the doctor~~
- learn to drive first • worry about them
- use their cars so much

Darren has had a headache for two weeks.

He ***should go to the doctor.***

He ***ought to go to the doctor.***

1 Pollution in towns is getting worse.
People ....
People ....

2 Martha has just eaten a big meal.
She ....
She ....

3 I want to run in the marathon next year.
You ....
You ....

4 Maria wants to buy a motorbike.
She ....
She ....

5 Jo and Tim are worried about their exams.
They ....
They ....

6 My bedroom is in a terrible mess.
You ....
You ....

7 Ben hasn't got any money.
He ....
He ....

8 That swimming pool is really dirty.
They ....
They ....

- **Verb *have to*: present simple, past simple**

2 Complete the statements and questions. Include the correct form of *have to* each time.

A: I ***had to*** stand on my head for ages in my last yoga lesson.

B: How long ***did you have to*** stand on your head?

1 A: We .... leave now.
B: Why .... now?

2 A: She .... get to school really early next Thursday.
B: What time .... get there?

3 A: I .... meet someone at the Rap Club now.
B: Who .... there?

4 A: She .... work all last weekend.
B: Why .... all last weekend?

5 A: You .... do your homework right now.
B: Why .... it now?

6 A: She .... pay a lot for her new computer. It was very expensive.
B: How much .... for it?

7 A: John .... spend weeks in hospital last summer.
B: How many ....
.... there?

8 A: Alan .... wash his dog really often.
B: How often .... it?

9 A: Teresa .... meet her mother now.
B: Where .... her?

10 A: We often .... bring things to draw to our art classes.
B: What sort of things ....
.... bring?

- ● **Verbs *have/has to* and *mustn't***

3 Read the rules at a holiday camp. Then complete Mr Martin's talk with *have/has to* or *mustn't*.

Lakeside Summer Camp

- Get up for breakfast at 8 a.m.
- Check the board for your job for the day.
- Tidy your room every day.
- Be on time for all classes and activities.
- No diving in the lake.
- Ask a teacher before using the windsurfers and canoes.
- Wear helmets when you use the canoes.
- Always take the windsurfers and canoes back to the boat house.
- Do not take food or drink into the computer room.
- Do not make a noise after 10 p.m.
- Always be kind and helpful to younger students.

Welcome to Lakeside Summer Camp. I'll quickly go through the most important rules. Breakfast is at eight. Everyone **has to** have it. After breakfast, you all ¹................. check the board in the dining room to find out your job for the day. The next thing you ²........................ do is quickly tidy your room and make your bed. Everyone ³.................... do this every day. After tidying your rooms, you ⁴............................. go to your morning activity or class. All the activities start at nine. You ⁵.............. be late. Our camp is next to a beautiful lake. You can swim in it, but

PLEASE REMEMBER, you ⁶................... dive in it. It is very dangerous. Before you take a windsurfer or canoe out on the lake, you ⁷................. ask a teacher. You ⁸................. go out in a canoe without a helmet. After using the canoes and windsurfers, you ⁹................. .... take them back to the boathouse. You ¹⁰...................... forget. If you are doing a computer course, you ¹¹......................... take food or drink into the computer rooms. You ¹²................. go outside if you want a snack. After ten at night, you ¹³................... turn your music down and you ¹⁴................... make a noise. A lot of you will be tired by then and you all ¹⁵................... get up quite early, so you really should go to sleep. Finally, I ask you all to remember that there are all ages of young people at this camp. Everyone ¹⁶...................... be kind and helpful to the younger campers.

- ● **Verbs *mustn't* and *don't/doesn't have to***

4 Choose the correct words in each sentence.

You (*mustn't*)/ *don't have to* read my diary. It's mine, not yours.

We *mustn't* / (*don't have to*) help with the school play, but we want to.

1 You *mustn't* / *don't have to* make a noise. My parents are asleep.

2 The Warrens have got a dishwasher. They *mustn't* / *don't have to* do the washing-up.

3 Lucy hasn't got a piano lesson tomorrow morning, so she *mustn't* / *doesn't have to* get up until ten.

4 That dog *mustn't* / *doesn't have to* sit on the sofa. He'll make it dirty.

5 You *mustn't* / *don't have to* ride your bike without a helmet. It's very dangerous.

6 Your sister can come on the picnic if she likes, but, of course, she *mustn't* / *doesn't have to*.

7 We *mustn't* / *don't have to* go to the Ice Club. We can go to a different place.

8 Dave *mustn't* / *doesn't have to* pay for cinema tickets because he's got a Saturday job at the ABC Cinema.

Practice

• Verbs *should, ought to, must* and *have to*

5 Choose the correct verb for each sentence.

You *should* / *have to* wear a swimming hat in this pool. You can't go in without one.

1 I *have to* / *must* get up at seven every morning to catch the 7.30 bus.

2 Most doctors say you *don't have to* / *shouldn't* lie in the sun too much.

3 Gary *mustn't* / *doesn't have to* pay much for air tickets. His brother works for an airline company.

4 How many languages *do you have to* / *must you* study at school in your country?

5 We *mustn't* / *don't have to* walk. We can take the bus if you're tired.

6 I *must* / *ought to* tidy my room today, but I'm not going to because I'm not in the mood.

7 I *didn't have to* / *mustn't* pay for the concert tickets. My boyfriend knows the band, so we got them free.

8 Don't worry. You *mustn't* / *don't have to* lend me your bike. I can borrow Dave's.

9 People *should* / *must* walk more and drive less. It's healthier and better for the environment.

10 This building is very dangerous and you *mustn't* / *shouldn't* go in there. If you do, I shall call the police.

• *Would you mind?* + gerund

6 Match the commands with the reasons. Then write polite requests with *Would you mind?*

Look after our goldfish.   [*i*]

1 Buy some aspirins.   ☐

2 Turn the music down.   ☐

3 Lend me your bike.   ☐

4 Open the window.   ☐

5 Open the door.   ☐

6 Make the dinner.   ☐

7 Help me with this suitcase.   ☐

8 Sign the visitors' book.   ☐

---

a) The cat wants to go out.

b) I'm late for school.

c) I'm too tired.

d) I'm trying to sleep.

e) It's terribly heavy.

f) It's one of the club rules.

g) It's very hot in here.

h) Mum's got a headache.

i) We're going on holiday.

Would you mind looking after our goldfish?
We're going on holiday.

1 ....

....

2 ....

....

3 ....

....

4 ....

....

5 ....

....

6 ....

....

7 ....

....

8 ....

....

9 They've been bullying me.

Present perfect continuous with *for* and *since*

Positive statements

Short form

I've been talking.
You've been talking.
He's been talking.
She's been talking.
We've been talking.
They've been talking.

Long form

I have been talking.
You have been talking.
He has been talking.
She has been talking.
We have been talking.
They have been talking.

> ● One use of the present perfect continuous is to talk about events and actions which began in the past and are still happening at the present moment.

Negative statements

Short form

I haven't been working.
You haven't been working.
He hasn't been working.
She hasn't been working.
We haven't been working.
They haven't been working.

Long form

I have not been working.
You have not been working.
He has not been working.
She has not been working.
We have not been working.
They have not been working.

Questions

Have I been waiting?
Have you been waiting?
Has he been waiting?
Has she been waiting?
Have we been waiting?
Have they been waiting?

> ● The present perfect continuous can be used to answer the question *How long?*, e.g. *How long have you been waiting? I've been waiting since eight o'clock/ for three hours. I haven't been waiting very long.*

Short answers

Positive

Yes, I/you have.
Yes, he/she has.
Yes, we/they have.

Negative

No, I/you haven't.
No, he/she hasn't.
No, we/they haven't.

Offers: *Would you like me to...? / Shall I...?*

Would you like me to carry that?
Shall I open the window?

• **Present perfect continuous with *for* and *since*: positive statements**

1 Choose the correct prompt for each picture. Write a sentence in the present perfect continuous with *for* or *since*.

> • look at the stars • cook • rain
> • ~~play in the snow~~ • revise for his exams
> • talk on her mobile • write her diary

1 hour

They've been playing in the snow for an hour.

1940

1 ....

9 o'clock

2 ....

2 hours

3 ....

5 days

4 ....

The day before yesterday

5 ....

2 months

6 ....

• **Present perfect continuous with *for* and *since*: questions and answers**

2 Write questions with *How long?* and the present perfect continuous, and answers with *for* or *since*, using the prompts.

Q: Nina / do / her exercises?

A: three o'clock

Q: *How long has Nina been doing her exercises?*

A: *Since three o'clock.*

1 **Q:** your mother / work / in the garden?

A: two hours

Q: ....

A: ....

2 **Q:** you / study / Chinese?

A: July

Q: ....

A: ....

3 **Q:** your granny / watch / that TV programme?

A: 1989

Q: ....

A: ....

4 **Q:** your brother / travel / around Asia?

A: a year

Q: ....

A: ....

5 **Q:** they / show / that film at the Ritz Cinema?

A: Wednesday

Q: ....

A: ....

6 **Q:** Sara / feel ill?

A: a week

Q: ....

A: ....

7 **Q:** he / work / at the swimming pool?

A: last summer

Q: ....

A: ....

8 **Q:** you / wait / for me?

A: 25 minutes

Q: ....

A: ....

● **Present perfect continuous with *for* and *since***

3 Match the activities with the time phrases. Then write sentences in the present perfect continuous.

People (watch) TV programmes ☐ `c`

1 Humans (live) on Earth ☐
2 People (travel) in space ☐
3 People (drive) cars ☐
4 Madonna (make) records ☐
5 Leonardo DiCaprio (work) as an actor ☐
6 People (write) ☐
7 People (ride) bicycles ☐
8 I (do) this exercise ☐

> a) 1790.
> b) about 5,000 years.
> c) about 60 years.
> d) about 1900.
> e) about five minutes.
> f) 1961.
> g) 1982.
> h) about 100,000 years.
> i) he was five.

People have been watching TV programmes
for about 60 years.

1 ....
....

2 ....
....

3 ....
....

4 ....
....

5 ....
....

6 ....
....

7 ....
....

8 ....
....

● **Present perfect continuous and past simple**

4 Complete the conversation by putting the verbs in brackets in the past simple or present perfect continuous.

Miranda: Sorry I'm late. How long
have you been waiting. (you / wait)?

Nick: Don't worry. I [1]............................
.... (not wait) very long.
I [2] .... (get) here about
ten minutes ago. By the way, why
is your hair wet? [3] ....
.... (it / rain)?

Miranda: Yes, it has. And I [4] .... (come)
by bike, so I got wet, of course.

Nick: How long [5]................................
(you / use) a bike to get around
London?

Miranda: I [6] .... (buy) this bike
two weeks ago and I [7]..................
.... (ride) it since then.
Are you OK, Nick? You look tired.

Nick: I [8] .... (not sleep)
well last night and I [9]..................
.... (feel) tired all day.

Miranda: Perhaps you need to do more sport.

Nick: I [10].......... (have) a riding lesson in
Richmond Park yesterday evening.

Miranda: Was that fun?

Nick: Yes, I [11] .... (enjoy) it.

Miranda: How long [12]................................
.... (you / learn) to ride?

Nick: About three months. You should
come with me some time.

Miranda: I think I prefer riding my bike.
It doesn't kick or bite!

• Offers: *Would you like me to?* and *Shall I?*

5 Complete the offers in the letter with *Would you like me ... ?* or *Shall I ... ?*
Then match Abby's offers with her grandmother's answers.

Dear Grandma

Mum tells me you're leaving for Mexico on Sunday. a) **_Would you like me_** to come and help you pack on Saturday? And how are you getting to the airport? b) .... give you a lift? Have you done all your holiday shopping? Or c) .... to buy you anything? Have you got a nice sunhat?

Or d) .... to lend you mine? What are you doing about your fish? I can look after them at our house if you like. e) .... come and collect them?

Have you told your friends in Mexico your plane times? Or f) .... e-mail them? How about books? g) .... to give you something to read on the beach? h) .... bring you my Spanish phrase book and dictionary? Call me soon,

Lots of love

Abby

1 ☐ ....
....

Yes, please. But that cat of yours mustn't go near them.

2 ☑ a   *Would you like me to come and help you pack on Saturday?*

No, thank you dear. I'm only taking one small suitcase.

3 ☐ ....
....

Yes, please. I want to try and learn some Spanish.

4 ☐ ....
....

It's OK. I've done all my shopping.

5 ☐ ....
....

That would be wonderful. But you mustn't drive too fast.

6 ☐ ....
....

Yes, please. Can you tell them my plane arrives on Monday at 11 a.m.?

7 ☐ ....
....

No, thanks. I've got three detective stories.

8 ☐ ....
....

No, thanks. I've got a nice, white baseball cap.

11 Unless I get to bed, ...

Grammar highlights

Verbs *will/won't*, *may* or *might* for predictions

Positive statements

We will be there at six. (It's definite.)
We'll bring Eva. (It's definite.)
Jackie may/might come too. (It's possible.)

Negative statements

We won't be late. (It's definite.)
We may/might not come by car. (It's possible.)

Questions	Short answers
Will we know anybody?	Yes, you will.
Will Andy be there?	He may/might.
Will there be a party after the match?	No, there won't.

- We use *will/won't* to talk about definite future events.
- We use *may/might* to talk about possible future events. There is no difference between *may* and *might* in this case.

- There is no short form of *may* or *might*.
- *Mightn't* is the short form of the negative *might not*.
  There is no short form of the negative *may not*.

First conditional: *if/unless* clause + *'ll (will)/won't*

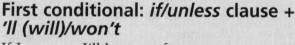

If I see one, I'll buy one for you.
I'll buy one for you if I see one.
If you don't leave now, you'll miss the train.
Unless you leave now, you'll miss the train.
You'll miss the train unless you leave now.
If you don't water the plants, they won't grow.

- The first conditional is used to describe a possible future event and its consequences.
- *If* or *unless* can introduce a first conditional clause. *Unless* means *if ... not*, e.g. *I won't phone if there isn't a problem. = I won't phone unless there's a problem.*
- In first conditional sentences, the verb in the *if/unless* clause is in the present simple tense. The verb in the main clause is often in the future simple tense (*will/won't*).
- *Will* and *won't* can be replaced in the main clause by *may (not)*, *might (not)* or *can*.
- When the *if/unless* clause comes first, we separate it from the main clause with a comma, e.g. *If I find the photo, I'll send it to you.*
- When the main clause comes first, there is no comma between it and the *if/unless* clause, e.g. *They may not come if the weather is bad. They won't cycle unless the weather is good.*

• Verbs *will/won't* for predictions

1 Complete Jackie's predictions using the verbs in the box with *will/won't*.

• ride   • be   • live   • come   • work
• use   • give   • make   • not be
• not   • have   • not leave   • not be

My ideas about the future
by Jackie Lewis

• In my opinion, one hundred years from now, the president of the United States
...will be... a woman.

• There ¹................. any oil or petrol in the world. So people ²................. cars or motorbikes. Everyone ³................. bikes or else they ⁴................. rollerblades.

• The sea level will be higher, but there ⁵................. enough drinking water. A lot of people ⁶................. in boats instead of houses.

• People ⁷................. their houses or boats very often. Offices and schools will close. Everyone ⁸................. at home. Teachers ⁹................. lessons over the Internet and TV.

• Scientists and doctors ¹⁰................. new body parts in laboratories.

• Martians ¹¹................. to Earth by spaceship for holidays.

• Verbs *will/won't, might* for predictions

2 Complete the conversations with *will, 'll, won't* or *might*. If both *'ll* and *will* are possible, use *'ll*.

1 A: When ..will.. my photos be ready?

   B: They probably ¹............. take very long. Two hours at the most, so they ²........... definitely be ready by four o'clock.

   A: How much ³........... they cost?

   B: Ten pounds, probably. But they ⁴................ be a little more. It depends.

   A: I see. I ⁵......... try to be back at two to pick them up. But I ⁶..................... be a bit late.

2 A: I'm worried about my driving test. I probably ⁷..................... be able to start the car!

   B: Don't be silly. Of course, you ⁸............ .

   A: ⁹............. you be angry if I don't pass?

   B: Yes, I ¹⁰............. ! I need you to drive me to the airport tomorrow!

3 A: I'm afraid you ¹¹............. be able to go out this evening. I want you to stay at home and look after Claire.

   B: Nick ¹²............. be annoyed with me.

   A: No, he ¹³............. . You can invite him here for the evening.

   B: I'm sure he ¹⁴............. come. He hates small children.

   A: I'm not so sure. He likes you, so he ¹⁵............. come. Why don't you call him and ask?

● First conditional with *if*

3 Match the sentence halves. Then write sentences in the first conditional.

Your Stars This Week By psychic sue

Aries March 21st to April 20th
Go out as much as possible. If you (stay) at home   [j]
If you stay at home, you won't meet that exciting new person.

1 Taurus April 21st to May 21st
Do some work. If you (not start) studying today,   ☐

2 Gemini May 22nd to June 21st
Be careful with your money. Your friend (not pay) you back   ☐

3 Cancer June 22nd to July 23rd
Do something different. If somebody (invite) you to a tango class,   ☐

4 Leo July 24th to August 23rd
Get busy in the kitchen. If you (make) dinner for everyone   ☐

5 Virgo August 24th to September 23rd
Be careful with your love letters. If your brother (find) them   ☐

6 Libra September 24th to October 23rd
You're feeling artistic. If you (take) a photo this week,   ☐

7 Scorpio October 24th to November 22nd
Think before you speak. Your best friend (be) very upset   ☐

8 Sagittarius November 23rd to December 21st
Take a trip this weekend. You (have) fun   ☐

9 Capricorn December 22nd to January 20th
Are you in love? Mr/Ms Right (not know) your feelings   ☐

10 Aquarius January 21st to February 19th
It's time to get fit. You (not die)   ☐

11 Pisces February 20th to March 20th
How's your health? If you (go) to bed early   ☐

a) ... you (feel) healthier.

b) ... you (fail) your exams in the summer.

c) ... if you (lend) her money.

d) ... he (read) them for sure!

e) ... if you say the wrong thing.

f) ... the whole family (love) you.

g) ... it (win) a prize!

h) ... if you (get) away from your home town for a bit.

i) ... you (go) for a run in the park!

j) ... you (not meet) that exciting new person.

k) ... if you (not tell) them.

l) ... you definitely (have fun).

- First conditional with *if/unless* clause

4 Write the advertisements, using the prompts with *if* or *unless* and the verbs in brackets.

ChickyBix
Biscuits for Dogs

If your dog likes chicken,
he'll love these biscuits.

your dog (like) chicken / he (love) these biscuits

LIVING DEAD

1 You (not enjoy) it / you (like) scary films

WATERWISE GOGGLES
For serious swimmers

2 You (not get) water in your eyes / you (wear) Waterwise goggles

Baby Come Back
This is a true story

3 It (make) you cry / you (have) a heart of stone

The Viking Alpine
The bike for top cyclists

4 you (want) to go up mountains / this bike (take) you to the top of them

The Rokia 222 Vision-Chat

TODAY'S MOBILE FOR TODAY'S PEOPLE. BUY YOURS TODAY!

5 you (buy) one today / we (give) you £10 free talk time

Are you tired of wearing heavy glasses?

With **FLOATS**, the Ultra Light glasses,

6 You (not know) you're wearing them / you (look) in the mirror

The **PANOS** Click
The camera that does everything for you

7 you (want) a camera that fits in your pocket / the Panos Click (be) right for you

Grammar highlights

The passive: present simple

Some jokes are told in every country.
These gates aren't locked at night.
Where is the sugar kept?
Paper is made from wood, isn't it?
Yes, it is.
Aren't you expected to do any homework?
No, I'm not.
The man in the photo is wanted by the police.

- The present simple passive is formed with the present tense of the verb *be* and the past participle of the main verb.

The passive: past simple

We were invited to a jazz concert.
She wasn't told about the broken window.
When were the Pyramids built?
This watch was given to me by my great-grandfather.
The telephone was invented by Bell, wasn't it?
Yes, it was.
Weren't the papers delivered this morning?
No, they weren't.

- The past simple passive is formed with the past tense of the verb *be* and the past participle of the main verb.

- We use the passive when we are more interested in the action or process than the person or thing that causes it, e.g. *A lot of money was stolen from the bank.* (= We don't know who stole it.) *Are the animals treated well?* (= It's not important who treats them well.)

- If we want to say who does the action or what causes it, we use *by*, e.g. *This picture was painted by a girl in my class.*

- We do not need to repeat the verb *be* if we are giving a list of actions in the passive, e.g. *The apples are washed, dried and delivered to the storeroom.*

• **Present and past simple passive: positive statements**

1 Match the sentence halves and write the complete sentence in the present or past simple passive.

The painting (sell) ... [g]

1 This letter (post) ... ☐
2 Lunch (serve) ... ☐
3 The film *Titanic* (show) again ... ☐
4 The front door (lock) ... ☐
5 The telephone (invent) ... ☐
6 Animals that (keep) ... ☐
7 These photos (take) ... ☐
8 A lot of plants (use) ... ☐

a) ... with my father's new camera.

b) ... at midnight every night.

c) ... in the hotel dining room at one o'clock every day.

d) ... in 1876 by Alexander Graham Bell.

e) ... in zoos often look sad.

f) ... last Monday.

g) (... last year for a million dollars.)

h) ... on television last week.

i) ... to make medicines even today.

The painting was sold last year for a
million dollars.

1 ....
....
2 ....
....
3 ....
....
4 ....
....
5 ....
....
6 ....
....
7 ....
....
8 ....
....

• **Present and past simple passive: questions and negative statements**

2 Rewrite these sentences in the passive.

They don't allow children under 16 in this club.

Children under 16 aren't allowed in this club.

1 They didn't tell us.
....

2 How much pocket money do they give you?
....

3 Why don't they give us more help?
....

4 They didn't invite you to this party.
....

5 When did they invent the camera?
....

6 Where did they hide the money?
....

7 When do they pay you?
....

8 They didn't give her a second chance.
....

9 Why didn't somebody turn the lights off?
....

10 They don't give the answers at the back of this book.
....
....

• Present and past simple passive: questions and answers

3 Match the questions to the answers. Check your answers below. Then write the full questions and answers in the present or past simple passive.

What Do You Know?

Q

When / the planet Pluto / discover?
1 When / the Great Wall of China / start?
2 When / television / invent?
3 What / cheese / make from?
4 What / chopsticks / use for?
5 Where / first Olympic Games / hold?
6 Which sport / invent in Japan in 1882?
7 When / Martin Luther King / assassinate?
8 When / the first man / send into space?
9 What / paper / make from?
10 Where / kilts / wear / by men?

A

a Greece
b 1926
c seventh century BC
d judo
e milk
f 1930

g Scotland
h 1968
i eating, in China and Japan, for example
j wood
k 1961

Q: *When was the planet Pluto discovered?*

A: *It was discovered in 1930.*

1 Q: ....
A: ....

2 Q: ....
A: ....

3 Q: ....
A: ....

4 Q: ....
A: ....

5 Q: ....
A: ....

6 Q: ....
A: ....

7 Q: ....
A: ....

8 Q: ....
A: ....

9 Q: ....
A: ....

10 Q: ....
A: ....

Answers

1c 2b 3e 4i 5a 6d 7h 8k 9j 10g

• Present and past simple passive

4 Complete the text, putting the verbs in brackets in the present or past simple, active or passive.

The most popular drink in the world

India, Sri Lanka and China _grow_ (grow) most of the world's tea. The tea plant can grow to 12 metres high, but it _is usually cut_ (usually cut) to 1.5 metres. The leaves [1] .... (not pick) until the plant is about five years old.

Tea [2] .... (produce) like this. First the tea leaves [3] .... (pick). Then they [4] .... (take) to special rooms to dry. They [5] .... (leave) in these rooms for a day. Then the leaves [6] .... (break) by machines. This [7] .... (allow) the oil to come out of the leaves. Next the leaves [8] .... (put) into ovens. When the tea leaves [9] .... (come) out of the ovens, they [10] .... (pack) in wooden boxes. Some of the tea [11] .... (export) and some of it [12] .... (keep) in the country where it was grown.

Tea [13] .... (probably discover) in China about 5,000 years ago. According to one story, Emperor Shang Yeng was drinking hot water in his garden when some leaves [14] .... (fall) off a wild tea bush into his cup. He [15] .... (love) the drink and soon tea bushes [16] .... (plant) all over China. For a long time, tea [17] .... (use) as money in China. In the fourteenth century, a good horse [18] .... (cost) about 68 kilos of tea.

Tea [19] .... (not bring) to England until 1657. At first only rich people [20] .... (drink) it because it was expensive. But it soon [21] .... (become) a very popular drink. Most people now [22] .... (make) tea with tea bags. In fact, every day in Britain, 150 million cups of tea [23] .... (make) from tea bags.

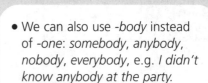

Grammar highlights

Pronouns: *someone, anyone, no one, everyone*

There's someone at the front door.
Has anyone seen my keys?
No one sent me a birthday card this year.
Has everyone got a ticket?

Pronouns: *something, anything, nothing, everything*

I've got something funny to tell you.
She didn't have anything interesting to say.
There's nothing for us to do in this town.
He gave everything to charity.

Pronouns: *somewhere, anywhere, nowhere, everywhere*

Let's go somewhere different this evening.
'Where shall we go?' 'Anywhere. You choose.'
The club was very crowded. There was nowhere to sit.
I've looked everywhere for my purse but I can't find it.

- We can also use *-body* instead of *-one*: *somebody, anybody, nobody, everybody*, e.g. *I didn't know anybody at the party.*
- Generally we use *someone, somebody, something* and *somewhere* in positive statements. We also use them in questions when we offer things, e.g. *Would you like something to drink?*
- Generally we use *anyone, anybody, anything* and *anywhere* in questions and negative statements.
- We use *anyone, anybody, anything* and *anywhere* when we mean 'it doesn't matter who, what, where,' e.g. *'Who shall I bring to your party?' 'Anyone.' 'What would you like to drink?' 'Anything.'*
- When we use the negative words *no one, nothing* and *nowhere*, we do not use a negative verb, e.g. *He did nothing.* (= He didn't do anything.) *I saw no one.* (= I didn't see anyone.)
- All these pronouns take singular verbs, e.g. *No one knows the answer. Everyone has to bring a notebook and pencil.* But we often use *their* and *they* after these pronouns, e.g. *Somebody has left their keys here.* (*their keys* = his or her keys)

Second conditional: *if* clause + *'d(would)/ wouldn't*

If I knew her address, I'd send her a birthday card.
It would take her an hour to get to school if she didn't have a bike.
If you could meet one famous person, who would you choose?
I wouldn't tell them about the party if I were you.

- We use the second conditional to talk about unreal or unlikely situations, or to give advice.
- *If I were you* is more common than *If I was you.*

- Pronouns: *some-, any-, no-, every-* + *thing, one, where*

1 Choose the correct pronoun in each sentence.

Have you got *something* / *everything* you need to make the cake?

1 *Everyone* / *No one* wants to die, but we all have to in the end.

2 Let's go *somewhere* / *anywhere* quiet to talk.

3 I can't tell you *nothing* / *anything* because it's a secret.

4 *Everyone's* / *Anyone's* talking about the new Will Smith film.

5 I don't want to say *something* / *anything* here. *Everyone* / *Anyone* is listening.

6 There was *somewhere* / *nowhere* to put my jacket, so I didn't take it off.

7 She's worried about *anything* / *something*, but she won't talk about it.

8 I can't see my glasses *somewhere* / *anywhere*. Can you help me to find them?

9 Please don't show *someone* / *anyone* these photos.

10 Her room is really untidy. There are clothes *anywhere* / *everywhere*.

11 What was that noise? I'm sure there's *anyone* / *someone* in the kitchen.

12 There's *nothing* / *something* to eat. Let's go out.

- **Second conditional**

2 Use the prompts to write sentences in the second conditional.

If I (be) you / I (not play) with those matches.

   If I were you, I wouldn't play with

   those matches.

1 If you (know) him better / you (not lend) him your tent.

   ....

   ....

2 What (you / do) / if you (find) £20 on the ground?

   ....

   ....

3 (you / spend) the money or (you / save) it / if you (win) £1,000?

   ....

   ....

4 Where (you / go) / if you (can) travel anywhere in the world?

   ....

   ....

5 I (not go) out with him / if I (be) her.

   ....

   ....

6 If I (not be) late for work / I (help) you.

   ....

   ....

7 If you (can) be anyone, anywhere, at any time in history / who (you / choose) to be?

   ....

   ....

8 I (not have) to help with the washing-up / if you (buy) a dishwasher

   ....

   ....

9 What (you / say) to Brad Pitt / if you (meet) him?

   ....

   ....

• **Second conditional**

3 Complete the quiz questions using the verbs in brackets. Then circle your reaction.

you (find) a frog on your bed

1 only three people (come) to your birthday party

2 a pet shop (offer) you a free pet

3 the music at your friend's party (be) terrible

4 you (have) to spend the night alone in a scary house

5 you (win) £1,000 in a competition

6 you (can) have a holiday anywhere in the world

7 you (go) to a restaurant with a very strange menu

ARE YOU ADVENTUROUS?

Find out with this quiz!

What would you do if you found a frog ....
on your bed? ....

a) scream

b) take a photo of it

c) kiss it. It could be a prince/princess.

1 ....

....

a) cry

b) tell them to go home

c) take them to a brilliant club

2 ....

....

a) choose a goldfish

b) choose a cat

c) choose a snake

3 ....

....

a) leave

b) change it

c) throw the CD in the bin

4 ....

....

a) faint

b) talk to friends all night on my mobile

c) stay awake hoping to see a ghost

5 ....

....

a) put it in the bank

b) spend £100 and save the rest

c) spend it all in a week

6 ....

....

a) go to a hotel in a European city

b) choose a beach holiday

c) visit the North Pole

7 ....

....

a) ask to leave

b) pretend to have a headache

c) order the grilled alligator and eat it

14 Someone had dropped it.

Grammar highlights

Past perfect simple

Positive statements
She had finished the job.
They'd already gone.

Negative statements
She hadn't made any mistakes.
They hadn't waited.

Questions
Had he opened his letters?
Hadn't they met before?
You'd already told him, hadn't you?

Short answers

Positive	Negative
Yes, he had.	No, he hadn't.
Yes, they had.	No, they hadn't.
Yes, I had.	No, I hadn't.

- We form the past perfect simple with the auxiliary *had* + the past participle.
- We use the past perfect simple tense to describe an event in the past that happened before another event in the past, e.g. *When I got there, he had left.* (= He left first; then I got there.) *She didn't want to come to the cinema because she had already seen the film.*

too many, too much, (not) enough

He couldn't understand the newspaper article because there were too many difficult words in it.
I left the concert because there was too much classical music and not enough jazz.
The film was boring because there weren't enough jokes.
She didn't enjoy the book because there wasn't enough humour.

- We use *too many* with plural countable nouns and *too much* with uncountable nouns. We use *(not) enough* with plural countable and uncountable nouns.

Reported requests and commands (verb + object + infinitive)

Positive

Direct speech	Reported speech
'Please help me.'	She wanted me to help her.
'Please give me a lift.'	She asked me to give her a lift.
'Drive carefully.'	She told me to drive carefully.

Negative

Direct speech	Reported speech
'Don't leave.'	He didn't want me to leave.
'Please don't tell anyone.'	He asked me not to tell anyone.
'Don't go too fast.'	He told me not to go too fast.

- We often use the imperative in direct requests and commands. We use the verbs *tell*, *ask* and *want* plus an object plus the infinitive with *to* when we want to report requests or commands.

Practice

• Past perfect simple: positive

1 Put the verbs in the past perfect simple.

We left the village of Moreton 15 years ago. Last week, I went back there for the first time. I was very shocked.

It **had changed** (change) a lot. It wasn't a village any more. It ¹.......................... (grow) into a town. They ².......................... (close) my old school. In its place, they ³.......................... (build) a sports centre. A lot of new shops ⁴.......................... (open) on the main street. My favourite toy shop ⁵.......................... (become) a mobile phone shop. They ⁶.......................... (plant) trees around the market square. They ⁷.......................... (make) Park Street wider. The Cup and Saucer café ⁸.......................... (move) from Park Street to New Road. The New Inn ⁹.......................... (become) The Moreton Motel. The people living in our old house ¹⁰.......................... (paint) it pink. And they ¹¹.......................... (put) a stupid sign on the front door – *The Pink House*. I didn't like the new Moreton, so I only spent an hour there. Then I got back on the train and came home.

• Past perfect simple: positive and negative

2 Complete each sentence with a verb from the box in the past perfect simple, positive or negative.

> • leave • see • eat • ~~break~~ • rain
> • fly • do • practise • miss

My mother was angry with my little brother because he **had broken** her coffee pot.

1 He didn't remember me because he
.... me for years.

2 There wasn't anything for lunch because the cat .... everything.

3 Suzie couldn't come out on Sunday evening because she ....
her homework.

4 My friend was nervous on the plane because she .... before.

5 I played badly in my piano lesson because I ....

6 She took a taxi home because she
.... the last bus.

7 It was easy to get into the house because they .... a window open on the ground floor.

8 All the plants in the garden were dead because it .... for months.

● **Past perfect or past simple**

3 Use the prompts to complete the sentences in two different ways. Use the past perfect and past simple in each pair of sentences.

I left the party early because

a) I (not know) anyone there

...*I didn't know anyone there.*...

b) I (agree) to meet Sophie at ten

...*I had agreed to meet Sophie at ten.*...

1 When I got to Sophie's place,

a) she (already leave)

....

b) I (cannot) find her

....

2 I began walking back to the party. I stopped when

a) I (walk) about 300 metres

....

b) I (see) a tall girl with a guitar

....

3 It was Natasha Ward.

a) I (not see) her for three years

....

b) She (be) really pleased to see me

....

4 I invited her to come to the party with me but

a) she (not like) the idea very much

....

b) she (already agree) to eat out with a friend

....

5 She invited me to come too and I agreed because

a) I (want) to get to know her better

....

b) I (not have) anything to eat all day

....

6 At the restaurant we met Natasha's friend. It was Sophie,

a) who (forget) about our plans for the evening

....

b) who (be) very surprised to see me with Natasha

....

● ***too many, too much, not enough***

4 Complete the sentences with *too many, too much, not enough* or *n't enough*.

He's not feeling well. He's eaten ...*too many*... carrots.

1 I can't take a photograph in this dark room. There is .... light.

2 You can't have a shower before we go out. There is .... time.

3 There are .... people in here. Can you all go and wait outside?

4 This coffee is too weak. I think you made it with .... water and .... coffee.

5 I'm not enjoying this book because it's too difficult. It's got .... long words that I don't understand.

6 You can't park the car there. There is .... space.

7 I spent .... money on holiday and now I haven't got any to spend on clothes.

5 Complete the doctor's comments with the present continuous of the verbs in brackets and *too many, too much* or *n't ... enough*.

– (take) exercise

You aren't taking enough exercise.

+ (eat) cakes and sweets

You're eating too many cakes and sweets.

1 – (get) fresh air

....

2 + (drink) coffee

....

3 + (have) late nights

....

4 – (do) exercise

....

5 – (eat) fruit and vegetables

....

6 + (do) work

....

Practice

- **Reported requests and commands**

6 Read the film director's notes. What did she tell each person to do?

ROLL-IT · FILM PRODUCTIONS

driver – pick me up at six on Thursday

secretary – don't give my mobile number to Justin

1 Trisha – change Penelope's makeup in the dance scene
2 Brad – don't be late on Friday
3 art director – don't change the colour of the curtains
4 scriptwriter – change Brad's first words in the beach scene
5 extras – don't move so much in the station scene
6 Penelope – ask Max for help with the dance

She told the driver to pick her up at six on Thursday.

She told the secretary not to give her mobile number to Justin.

1 ....
....
2 ....
....
3 ....
....
4 ....
....
5 ....
....
6 ....
....

- **Reported requests and commands**

7 Match the requests in boxes a) to i) with the sentence beginnings. Then complete each sentence with the correct reported request.

[h] Lucy was making a terrible noise so I told *her to be quiet.* ....

1 ☐ I wanted to have a shower so I told
....

2 ☐ Mick was driving very fast so I told
....

3 ☐ Maria was upset about her exam so I told
....

4 ☐ I couldn't hear the teacher so I asked
....

5 ☐ The goldfish were very hungry so I asked
....

6 ☐ They had dirty hands so I didn't want
....

7 ☐ I was really hungry so I didn't want
....

8 ☐ Pete and I were going to a sixties party and we wanted ....

a) | Can you feed them, Andy?

b) | Can you take a photo of us, Irma?

c) | Could you repeat the question please, Sir?

d) | Don't be too long in the bathroom, Dave.

e) | Don't eat all the spaghetti, Simon.

f) | Don't touch my drawings.

g) | Don't worry!

(h) | Please be quiet!

i) | Slow down!

16 They used to hunt buffalo.

Remember....

Verb *used to*

Positive statements

I used to have short hair (but I've grown it).
There used to be a school here (but there isn't now).
She used to work in a shop (but she doesn't now).

Negative statements

I didn't use to have long hair (but I do now).
There didn't use to be a cinema here (but there is now).
She didn't use to work in a restaurant (but she does now).

Questions

Did you use to like having short hair?
Didn't there use to be a cinema here?
Where did she use to work?

Short answers

Positive	Negative
Yes, I did.	No, I didn't.
Yes, there did.	No, there didn't.

- We use *used to* to talk about things which were true in the past but are not true now.

so and *such a/an* + adjective + noun for exclamations

She's so good at art!
She's such a good painter!
It was such an amazing holiday!
There were such exciting activities!

- We use *so* with an adjective and *such (a/an)* with an adjective followed by a noun.

so and *such* with a clause of result

He was so surprised (that) he couldn't speak.
They were so happy (that) they danced in the street.
It was such a boring book (that) I couldn't read it.
They were such stupid jokes (that) nobody laughed at them.

- When we use *so* or *such* in result clauses, we can omit *that*, e.g. *The book was so boring that I couldn't read it. It was such a boring book that I couldn't read it.* Or: *The book was so boring I couldn't read it. It was such a boring book I couldn't read it.*

● *Used to*: positive and negative statements

1 Write the sentences with *used to/didn't use to* and the present or past simple.

He (play) a lot of football but now he just (watch) it on TV.

He used to play a lot of football but now he just watches it on TV.

1 She (not like) tea but she (drink) a lot of it these days.

2 There (be) a lot of cars in this town but now everybody (ride) bicycles.

3 He (not take) any exercise but now he (go) for a run every day.

4 My grandparents (not travel) outside the UK but last year they (go) to Spain for the first time.

5 We (have) a dog but it (die) a year ago.

6 You (talk) all the time but you (be) very quiet these days.

7 People (read) a lot in their free time but now they (watch) TV.

8 Sandra (live) in Bristol but she (move) to Penzance last month.

● *Used to*: positive and negative statements

2 Use the prompts to write sentences with *used to/didn't use to ... but now she doesn't/does*.

Alice went to work on a sheep farm in Australia last year and her life changed a lot.

Before, she ...

lived in a smart flat in London.

1 worked in an office on the 33rd floor.

2 had an expensive car.

3 wore designer clothes.

4 went out to clubs and restaurants a lot.

She used to live in a smart flat in London, but now she doesn't.

1 ....

2 ....

3 ....

4 ....

Now, she ...

lives 60 kilometres from the nearest house.

5 starts work at six every morning.

6 has a horse.

7 wears jeans and a T-shirt every day.

8 goes to bed at ten o'clock.

She didn't use to live 60 kilometres from the nearest house, but now she does.

5 ....

6 ....

7 ....

8 ....

● *Used to*: question forms

3 Read the text. Then write the interviewer's questions, using a verb from the box in the present simple or with *use to*.

• live • dream • drive • ~~get~~

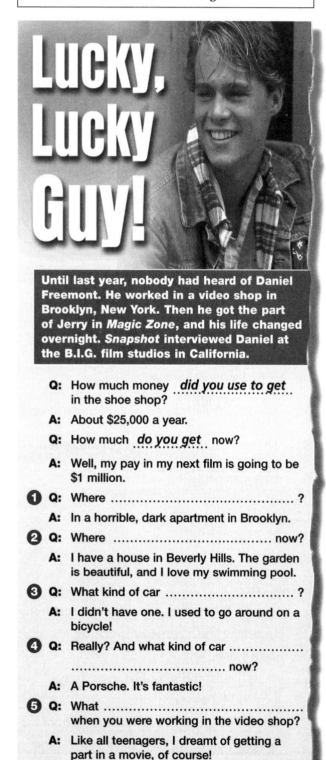

Lucky, Lucky Guy!

Until last year, nobody had heard of Daniel Freemont. He worked in a video shop in Brooklyn, New York. Then he got the part of Jerry in *Magic Zone*, and his life changed overnight. *Snapshot* interviewed Daniel at the B.I.G. film studios in California.

Q: How much money *did you use to get* in the shoe shop?

A: About $25,000 a year.

Q: How much *do you get* now?

A: Well, my pay in my next film is going to be $1 million.

❶ Q: Where .... ?

A: In a horrible, dark apartment in Brooklyn.

❷ Q: Where .... now?

A: I have a house in Beverly Hills. The garden is beautiful, and I love my swimming pool.

❸ Q: What kind of car .... ?

A: I didn't have one. I used to go around on a bicycle!

❹ Q: Really? And what kind of car ....
.... now?

A: A Porsche. It's fantastic!

❺ Q: What ....
when you were working in the video shop?

A: Like all teenagers, I dreamt of getting a part in a movie, of course!

❻ Q: And what .... now?

A: I dream of having a holiday for a year!

● *Used to*: all forms

4 Complete the conversation between Lucy and her great-grandmother, Joyce, with the correct form of *used to*.

Joyce: Things have changed a lot here during my lifetime. I was born here 95 years ago. And it <u>used to</u> be a much smaller and quieter place.

Lucy: ¹............ people .... drive slowly through the town?

Joyce: Well, 80 years ago, it was a village, not a town. There ²............................. be many cars – only about ten people had them. And the policeman ³................................. ride a bike.

Lucy: ⁴............ there only .... be one policeman?

Joyce: Yes! That was when I was 15. In those days, my friends and I ⁵......................... get the bus to Bristol once a week to go to the cinema. They ⁶........................... show black-and-white films. We ⁷................................. see horrible violent films like the ones today.

Lucy: ⁸................ you .... like Charlie Chaplin films?

Joyce: Yes, dear. We loved them.

Lucy: And what ⁹.............. Grandpa .... do? ¹⁰.............. he .... go to the cinema?

Joyce: Sometimes. But he was more interested in sport. The boys all ¹¹............................ play cricket on the village green every Sunday in the summer. And the girls ¹²......................
.... sit on the grass and watch.

Lucy: ¹³.................... you .... enjoy watching Grandpa play cricket?

Joyce: Yes, dear. Of course I did. Your grandfather ¹⁴.............. be a very good-looking young man. After the match, I sometimes ¹⁵.............. go to the village shop and buy a drink. A lemonade only ¹⁶.............. cost a penny in those days. My friend Edith ¹⁷.............. work in the shop, and we ¹⁸............. talk about everything. Face to face, of course. Not on the phone. We weren't like young people today. We ¹⁹.............
.... have these silly mobile phone things.

• **Exclamations with *so, such a/an***

5 Complete the sentences with *so, such* or *such a/an*.

Why have you made ...*such a*.. big cake?

1 You are .... tall for thirteen. You look about eighteen!

2 It was a great holiday. We had .... brilliant time.

3 The film was extremely silly. I've never seen .... stupid film.

4 She's .... clever. She always gets the highest marks in the class.

5 He's really nice and he's got .... nice smile.

6 She always looks .... tired. I think she works very hard.

7 He's often very late. It's because he lives .... long way from the school.

8 Don't be .... annoying! Leave me alone.

9 They are .... nice people. They are always .... helpful and kind.

10 These are .... interesting photos. You must look at them.

11 Don't be .... lazy! Turn the TV off and come and play tennis.

• **Result clauses with *so* and *such***

6 Match the sentence halves. Then join them with *so/such ... that*.

It was a funny book. $\boxed{c}$

The film was boring. $\boxed{f}$

1 It was a lovely day. ☐

2 The music was loud. ☐

3 It was delicious food. ☐

4 He's a liar. ☐

5 The sea was clear and blue. ☐

6 It was a wonderful moment. ☐

7 The sand was hot. ☐

8 The boat trips were cheap. ☐

---

a) I couldn't sleep.

b) I don't believe anything he says.

c) I fell off my chair laughing.

d) I'll never forget it.

e) They decided to go to the beach.

f) They fell asleep in the middle of it.

g) We went on one every day.

h) We couldn't stop eating it.

i) We had to dive in immediately.

j) We had to run across it.

It was such a funny book that I fell off my chair laughing.

The film was so boring that they fell asleep in the middle of it.

1 ....
....

2 ....
....

3 ....
....

4 ....
....

5 ....
....

6 ....
....

7 ....
....

8 ....
....

Remember....

Grammar highlights

Reported statements

Direct speech

'He is French.'
'We're having fun.'
'I like chocolate.'
'They arrived on Tuesday.'
'I've found my purse.'
'We'll leave on Sunday.'
'I can't wait.'

Reported speech

He said (that) he was French.
They said (that) they were having fun.
She said (that) she liked chocolate.
I told her (that) they had arrived on Tuesday.
She said (that) she had found her purse.
They told me (that) they would leave on Sunday.
She told us (that) she couldn't wait.

- This chart shows the rules for tense changes after a past reporting verb such as *said* or *told*.

Direct speech		Reported speech
Present continuous	→	Past continuous
Present simple	→	Past simple
Past simple	→	Past perfect
Present perfect	→	Past perfect
can/will/may	→	*could/would/might*

- The word *that* can be omitted, e.g. *She said she hadn't had a good time.*

- *Tell* is always followed by an object pronoun or noun, e.g. *He told her he'd be late. He told Susie he'd be late.* If you use *say* and you want to mention who the speaker was talking to, you have to use *to*, e.g. *He said (to Susie) that he'd be late.*

- After a present tense reporting verb such as *say(s)*, *tell(s)*, there are no tense changes, e.g. *'I'm hungry.' She says that she is hungry.*

Practice

● **Reported statements**

1 Report what top ballet dancer Claudia Ross said in a recent interview.

> Most of my friends are dancers.
>
> 1 I was in Sydney in January and New York in February.
>
> 2 I don't really like travelling all over the world.
>
> 3 I won't be a dancer in ten years' time.
>
> 4 As a dancer, I can't eat chips and chocolate.
>
> 5 I have to get eight hours' sleep a night.
>
> 6 I always eat a lot of fruit and vegetables.
>
> 7 My parents didn't want me to be a professional dancer.
>
> 8 I started dancing when I was 16.
>
> 9 I'll probably train as a dance teacher one day.

She said most of her friends were dancers.

1 ....

2 ....

3 ....

4 ....

5 ....

6 ....

7 ....

8 ....

9 ....

● **Reported speech**

2 Read the newspaper article. Write singer Johnny Rowland's actual words to the reporter.

Music News

Johnny Rowland's Secret Love!

Singer Johnny Rowland told reporters at his home in Miami, Florida, that *his life was going really well*. [1]He said he had fallen in love and he was now a different person. [2]He said that he wouldn't tell anyone her name yet. [3]But he said she was the most beautiful girl in the world. [4]He added that they were going to get married soon. [5]He said he couldn't give the exact date because it was a secret. [6]He said that he was releasing a new album in June. [7]He said that he would never stop singing and playing because he loved music more than anything.

' *My life is going really well.* '

1 ' ....
   .... '

2 ' ....
   .... '

3 ' ....
   .... '

4 ' ....
   .... '

5 ' ....
   .... '

6 ' ....
   .... '

7 ' ....
   .... '

● **Reported statements**

3 Write what Justin and Rosie said about their evening.

Justin

> Rosie asked to come ice-skating with me.
> 1 She was an hour late.
> 2 She didn't bring any money.
> 3 She can't skate at all.
> 4 Rosie doesn't even try to learn.
> 5 I'm not inviting her out again.
> 6 I'll go skating on my own in future.
> 7 I've never met a more annoying girl.

Rosie

> I went out with Justin to be kind.
> 1 He arrived an hour early.
> 2 Justin pretends to be really rich.
> 3 He only talks about skating.
> 4 He's a really bad teacher.
> 5 I can't remember a worse evening.
> 6 I won't ever go out with him again.
> 7 I don't like bossy people like Justin.

Justin said *Rosie had asked to come ice-skating with him.* ....

Rosie said *she had gone out with Justin to be kind.* ....

1 Justin said ....

   Rosie said ....

2 Justin said ....

   Rosie said ....

3 Justin said ....

   Rosie said ....

4 Justin said ....

   Rosie said ....

5 Justin said ....

   Rosie said ....

6 Justin said ....

   Rosie said ....

7 Justin said ....

   Rosie said ....

18 Jamaica Inn

Grammar highlights

Reported questions

Direct questions

_Wh-_ questions

'What's your telephone number?'
'Where do you work?'
'When did you arrive?'
'Where have you left your bags?'

Yes/No questions

'Do you like your job?'
'Did you go to Sue's party?'
'Will you speak to Sam?'
'Can I get you a drink?'
'Have you bought a ticket?'

Reported questions

_Wh-_ questions

He asked her what her telephone number was.
He asked her where she worked.
He asked her when she had arrived.
He asked her where she had left her bags.

Yes/No questions

He asked her if she liked her job.
He asked her if she had gone to Sue's party.
He asked her if she would speak to Sam.
He asked her if he could get her a drink.
He asked her if she had bought a ticket.

- The rules for tense changes in reported questions are the same as in reported statements.

- There are no tense changes after a reporting word in the present tense, e.g. _'What kind of music do you like?'_ I often ask people what kind of music they like.

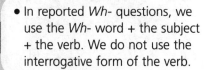

- In reported _Wh-_ questions, we use the _Wh-_ word + the subject + the verb. We do not use the interrogative form of the verb.

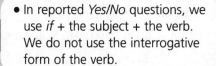

- In reported _Yes/No_ questions, we use _if_ + the subject + the verb. We do not use the interrogative form of the verb.

- **Reported questions: *Wh-* questions**

1 Write who asked you each question and report the question.

- my boyfriend • my dad • my dog
- my Maths teacher • my mum
- ~~the hairdresser~~ • the waitress

How often do you wash your hair?
The hairdresser asked me how often I washed my hair.

1 What kind of pizza do you want?
....
....

2 Where did you buy the CD?
....
....

3 When are we going for a walk?
....
....

4 How will you get back from the party?
....
....

5 Why haven't you done your homework?
....
....

6 Who has drunk all the orange juice?
....
....

- **Reported questions: *Yes/No* questions**

2 Decide which person in the box asked each prompt question. Then complete the reported questions.

- best friend • brother • ~~taxi driver~~
- parents • customs officer • PE teacher
- shop assistant

Do you want to get out at the corner?

The *taxi driver* asked Jack *if he wanted to get out at the corner.*

1 Is the blue jacket the right size?

The .... asked me ....
....

2 Did you buy any watches or cameras during your holiday?

The .... asked the man ....
....

3 Will you be free to play in the match on Saturday?

The .... asked Laura ....
....

4 Do you want a camera for your birthday?

Her .... asked her ....
....

5 Have you bought anything for Mum's birthday?

My .... asked me ....
....

6 Are you going to invite Sonia to the school disco?

Neil's .... asked him ....
....

• **Reported questions: mixed**

3 Write the direct questions as reported questions.

He asked if they had any toothpaste.
She asked what kind of toothpaste he was
looking for.

3 ....
....
....

1 ....
....
....

4 ....
....
....

2 ....
....
....

5 ....
....
....

19 He's too good to fall.

Grammar highlights

too + adjective/adverb + *to*
She's too clever to make that mistake again.
She thinks too clearly to make that mistake.

- *Too* goes before an adjective or adverb.
- *Enough* goes after an adjective or adverb.

(not) + adjective/adverb + *enough to*
He wasn't quick enough to catch the ball.
He didn't run quickly enough to catch the ball.
He's stupid enough to believe anything.

Verb + infinitive with *to*
She offered to pay.
We agreed to do it.
They seemed to like the present.

These verbs take an infinitive with *to*:

decide, want, offer, promise, hope, agree, seem, manage, refuse, expect, learn, remember, forget, ask

Verb + gerund (*-ing* form)
I don't mind helping.
They've finished cleaning the room.
We couldn't avoid seeing them.

These verbs take a gerund:
mind, enjoy, miss, finish, give up, avoid, practise, like, hate, love, stop

• *Too* + adjective/adverb + *to*

1 Join the two sentences using *too … to*.

The sea is very dangerous. We can't swim here.

The sea is too dangerous to swim here.

1 I was very tired. I couldn't finish my homework last night.

....

....

2 Her car is very small. It can't take five people.

....

....

3 She speaks very quietly. She can't become an actress.

....

....

4 Martin's very busy. He can't help me with the cooking.

....

....

5 It's very dark. I can't read in this room.

....

....

6 You drive very dangerously. You won't pass your test.

....

....

7 She's very short. She can't become a model.

....

....

8 This book is very difficult. I can't understand it.

....

....

9 He sings very badly. He can't be in a band.

....

....

• *(not)* + adjective/adverb + *enough to …*

2 Read the article. Then write sentences about yourself with *I'm (not) old enough to.*

Young people and the law

In Britain you can:

be arrested by the police at ten
1 buy a pet without your parents' permission at 12
2 get a part-time job at 13
3 work full time at 16
4 get married with your parents' permission at 16
5 join the army, if you're a boy, at 16
   join the army, if you're a girl, at 17
6 drive a car or motorbike at 17
7 vote at 18

Name:................................ Age: ......

Male/Female: ....

In Britain:

I'm old enough to be arrested by the police.

1 ....

....

2 ....

....

3 ....

....

4 ....

....

5 ....

....

6 ....

....

7 ....

....

- *too ... to / not ... enough to*

3 Complete the answers using *too* or *n't ... enough to* with the words in brackets.

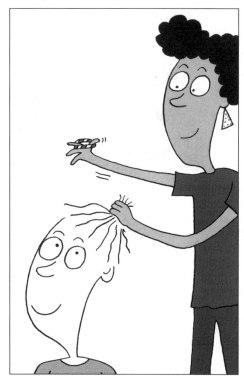

Shall I put your hair in a ponytail? (long)
No, it is**n't long enough to put in a ponytail.**

1 Is he a sports teacher? (healthy)
No, he is ....
....

2 Did they do a parachute jump? (brave)
No, they were ....
....

3 Did she buy the necklace? (poor)
No, she was ....
....

4 Did you go surfing? (scared)
No, we were ....
....

5 Did they swap telephone numbers? (shy)
No, they were ....
....

6 Did you take a photo inside the castle? (light)
No, it was ....
....

- *too ... to / n't (not) ... enough to*

4 Complete the e-mail using *too ... to* or *n't ... enough to* with an adjective from the box.

- calm   • ~~cold~~   • crowded   • expensive   • far   • nervous
- old   • small   • sociable   • strong   • windy

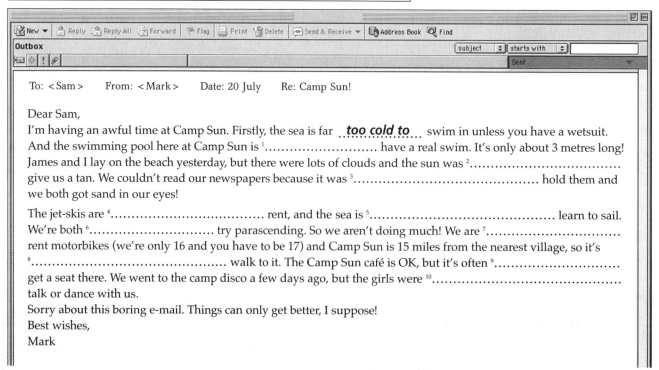

To: <Sam>   From: <Mark>   Date: 20 July   Re: Camp Sun!

Dear Sam,
I'm having an awful time at Camp Sun. Firstly, the sea is far   **too cold to**   swim in unless you have a wetsuit.
And the swimming pool here at Camp Sun is [1].......................... have a real swim. It's only about 3 metres long!
James and I lay on the beach yesterday, but there were lots of clouds and the sun was [2]...................................
give us a tan. We couldn't read our newspapers because it was [3].. hold them and
we both got sand in our eyes!

The jet-skis are [4].................................... rent, and the sea is [5].. learn to sail.
We're both [6]............................ try parascending. So we aren't doing much! We are [7]............................
rent motorbikes (we're only 16 and you have to be 17) and Camp Sun is 15 miles from the nearest village, so it's
[8]... walk to it. The Camp Sun café is OK, but it's often [9]...........................
get a seat there. We went to the camp disco a few days ago, but the girls were [10]...
talk or dance with us.
Sorry about this boring e-mail. Things can only get better, I suppose!
Best wishes,
Mark

• **too ... to / not ... enough to**

5 Make two sentences into one sentence using *too ... to* or *not enough to*.

She was driving very fast; she couldn't stop in time.
She was driving too fast to stop in time.

He wasn't driving very slowly; he didn't see the name of the street.
He wasn't driving slowly enough to see the name of the street.

1 He drives very aggressively; he isn't a good driver.

....

....

2 He didn't jump very high; he didn't break the record.

....

....

3 They all got up very late; they couldn't catch the early bus.

....

....

4 I couldn't see very clearly; I couldn't read the time on the clock.

....

....

5 We didn't wake up very early; we didn't see the sunrise.

....

....

6 He types very slowly; he can't get a job as a secretary.

....

....

• **Verb followed by infinitive or gerund**

6 Complete the sentences, putting the verbs into the correct form: infinitive or gerund.

Maria always enjoys _singing_ (sing) at parties.

1 He doesn't exactly lie. But he avoids .... (answer) any of my questions.

2 Have they agreed .... (start) work on Monday?

3 She's decided .... (study) in the USA.

4 I didn't expect .... (meet) Rob in Florida.

5 At last they've finished .... (paint) their house.

6 My brother has given up .... (collect) stamps.

7 We hope .... (visit) them next summer.

8 Did you manage .... (finish) your Science project?

9 I used to live by the sea. Now I miss .... (go) swimming every day.

10 He practises .... (play) the guitar every day. He wants to be in a band.

11 They didn't mind .... (pay) for dinner. They've got lots of money.

12 Sandra has offered .... (take) us to the airport.

13 She promised .... (phone) every day, but she hasn't phoned once.

14 Why did you refuse .... (go) out with Jerry? He's really nice.

15 She seems .... (be) very popular.

16 Do you want .... (come) for a picnic with us on Sunday?

Irregular verbs

Infinitive	Past simple	Past participle
be	was	been
become	became	become
begin	began	begun
bite	bit	bitten
blow (out)	blew (out)	blown (out)
break	broke	broken
bring	brought	brought
build	built	built
buy	bought	bought
catch	caught	caught
choose	chose	chosen
come	came	come
cost	cost	cost
cut	cut	cut
do	did	done
draw	drew	drawn
drink	drank	drunk
drive	drove	driven
eat	ate	eaten
fall	fell	fallen
feed	fed	fed
feel	felt	felt
fight	fought	fought
find	found	found
fly	flew	flown
forget	forgot	forgotten
get	got	got
give	gave	given
go	went	gone
grow	grew	grown
have	had	had
hear	heard	heard
hit	hit	hit
hold	held	held
hurt	hurt	hurt
keep	kept	kept
know	knew	known
learn	learnt	learnt
leave	left	left
lend	lent	lent
lose	lost	lost
make	made	made
meet	met	met
pay	paid	paid
put	put	put
read	read	read
ride	rode	ridden
ring	rang	rung
run	ran	run
say	said	said
see	saw	seen
sell	sold	sold
send	sent	sent

Infinitive	Past simple	Past participle
shine	shone	shone
shut	shut	shut
sing	sang	sung
sit	sat	sat
sleep	slept	slept
speak	spoke	spoken
spend	spent	spent
split up	split up	split up
stand	stood	stood
steal	stole	stolen
swim	swam	swum
take	took	taken
teach	taught	taught
tell	told	told
think	thought	thought
throw	threw	thrown
understand	understood	understood
wake (up)	woke (up)	woken (up)
wear	wore	worn
weep	wept	wept
win	won	won
write	wrote	written